James Whitcomb Riley.

AMERICAN
WIT AND HUMOR

BY

ONE HUNDRED OF AMERICA'S
LEADING HUMORISTS

INTRODUCTION BY
JOEL CHANDLER HARRIS

INCLUDING
WORLD FAMOUS CARTOONS AND CARICATURES

NEW YORK
THE REVIEW OF REVIEWS CO.
1907

THE QUINN & BODEN PRESS
RAHWAY, N. J.

Table of Contents

American Wit and Humor

Table of Contents

American Wit and Humor

Table of Contents

Acknowledgments

Acknowledgments and thanks are gratefully made to the following publishers for permitting the use of selections appearing in this volume:

BOBBS-MERRILL COMPANY, Indianapolis: "The Elf-Child," "A Liz-Town Humorist," "When the Frost is on the Punkin," "A Old Played-Out Song," by JAMES WHITCOMB RILEY.

SMALL, MAYNARD & CO., Boston: "Tale of the Kennebec Mariner," "Cure for Homesickness," "Grampy Sings a Song," "John W. Jones," "The Ballad of Doc Pluff," "A Settin' Hen," by HOLMAN F. DAY; "On Gold-Seeking," "On Expert Testimony," by F. P. DUNNE (Mr. Dooley); Selections from "Letters from a Self-Made Merchant to His Son," by GEORGE HORACE LORIMER.

F. A. STOKES & CO., New York: "The Bohemians of Boston," by FRANK GELETT BURGESS.

H. S. STONE & CO., Chicago: "The Fable of the Preacher who Flew his Kite," etc., "The Fable of the Caddy who Hurt his Head While Thinking," "The Fable of the Two Mandolin Players and the Willing Performer," by GEORGE ADE.

R. H. RUSSELL, New York: "Home Life of Geniuses," "The City as a Summer Resort," "Avarice and Generosity," "Work and Sport," by F. P. DUNNE (Mr. Dooley).

GEORGE W. DILLINGHAM COMPANY, New York: "John Henry at the Musicale," "John Henry at the Races," by GEORGE V. HOBART.

HOUGHTON, MIFFLIN & CO., Boston: "Caffiard," by GUY WETMORE CARRYL; "Borrowing a Hammer," by MARY N. MURFREE (Charles Egbert Craddock); "An Old War-Horse to a Young Politician," by WILLIAM H. McELROY.

FORBES & CO., Chicago: "The Pessimist," "If I Should Die To-Night," by BEN KING.

DUQUESNE DISTRIBUTING COMPANY, Harman-ville, Pa.: "In Society," by WILLIAM J. KOUNTZ, JR. (Billy Baxter).

BACHELLER, JOHNSON & BACHELLER, New York: "The Composite Ghost," by MARION COUTHOUY SMITH.

American Wit and Humor

American Wit and Humor

James Whitcomb Riley

When the Frost is on the Punkin

WHEN the frost is on the punkin and the fodder's in the shock,
And you hear the kyouck and gobble of the struttin' turkey-
      cock,
And the clackin' of the guineys, and the cluckin' of the hens,
And the rooster's hallylooyer as he tiptoes on the fence;
Oh, it's then's the times a feller is a-feelin' at his best,
With the risin' sun to greet him from a night of peaceful rest,
As he leaves the house, bare-headed, and goes out to feed the
      stock,
When the frost is on the punkin and the fodder's in the shock.

They's something kindo' harty-like about the atmusfere
When the heat of summer's over and the coolin' fall is here—
Of course we miss the flowers, and the blossoms on the trees,
And the mumble of the hummin'-birds and buzzin' of the bees;
But the air's so appetizin'; and the landscape through the
      haze
Of a crisp and sunny morning of the airly autumn days
Is a pictur' that no painter has the colorin' to mock—
When the frost is on the punkin and the fodder's in the shock.

The husky, rusty russel of the tossels of the corn,
And the raspin' of the tangled leaves, as golden as the morn;
The stubble in the furries—kindo' lonesome-like, but still
A-preachin' sermuns to us of the barns they growed to fill;

3

The straw stack in the medder, and the reaper in the shed;
The hosses in theyr stalls below—the clover overhead!—
Oh, it sets my hart a-clickin' like the tickin' of a clock,
When the frost is on the punkin and the fodder's in the
    shock!

Then your apples all is getherd, and the ones a feller keeps
Is poured around the celler-floor in red and yeller heaps;
And your cider-makin' 's over, and your wimmern-folks is
    through
With their mince and apple-butter, and theyr souse and saus-
    sage, too! . . .
I don't know how to tell it—but ef sich a thing could be
As the Angels wantin' boardin', and they'd call around on
    me—
I'd want to 'commodate 'em—all the whole-indurin' flock—
When the frost is on the punkin and the fodder's in the shock!

Used by special permission of the publishers, The Bobbs-Merrill Company. "From Neighborly Poems," copyright, 1897.

A Old Played-Out Song

It's the curiousest thing in creation,
    Whenever I hear that old song
"Do They Miss Me at Home," I'm so bothered,
    My life seems as short as it's long!—
Fer ev'rything 'pears like adzackly
    It 'peared in the years past and gone—
When I started out sparkin', at twenty,
    And had my first neckercher on!

James Whitcomb Riley

Though I'm wrinkelder, older, and grayer
   Right now than my parents was then,
You strike up that song "Do They Miss Me,"
   And I'm jest a youngster again!—
I'm a-standin' back thare in the furries
   A-wishin' fer evening to come,
And a-whisperin' over and over
   Them words "Do They Miss Me at Home?"

You see, *Marthy Ellen she* sung it
   The first time I heerd it; and so,
As she was my very first sweethart,
   It reminds me of her, don't you know—
How her face ust to look, in the twilight,
   As I tuck her to Spellin'; and she
Kep' a-hummin' that song tel I ast her,
   Pine-blank, ef she ever missed *me!*

I can shet my eyes now, as you sing it,
   And hear her low answerin' words;
And then the glad chirp of the crickets,
   As clear as the twitter of birds;
And the dust in the road is like velvet,
   And the ragweed and fennel and grass
Is as sweet as the scent of the lilies
   Of Eden of old, as we pass.

"Do They Miss Me at Home?" Sing it lower—
   And softer—and sweet as the breeze
That powdered our path with the snowy
   White bloom of the old locus' trees!

Let the whipperwills he'p you to sing it,
    And the echoes 'way over the hill,
Tel the moon boolges out, in a chorus
    Of stars, and our voices is still.

But oh, "They's a chord in the music
    That's missed when *her* voice is away!"
Though I listen from midnight tell morning,
    And dawn tel the dusk of the day!
And I grope through the dark, lookin' up'ards
    And on through the heavenly dome,
With my longin' soul singin' and sobbin'
    The words "Do They Miss Me at Home?"

Used by special permission of the publishers, The Bobbs-Merrill Company. "From Neighborly Poems," copyright, 1897.

The Elf-Child

LITTLE Orphant Annie's come to our house to stay,
An' wash the cups and saucers up, an' brush the crumbs away,
An' shoo the chickens off the porch, an' dust the hearth an'
    sweep
An' make the fire, an' bake the bread, an' earn her board an'
    keep;
An' all us other children, when the supper things is done,
We set around the kitchen fire an' has the mostest fun
A-listenin' to the witch tales 'at Annie tells about,
An' the Gobble-uns 'at gits you

                    Ef you
                        Don't
                            Watch
                                Out!

James Whitcomb Riley

Onct they was a little boy who wouldn't say his prayers—
An' when he went to bed at night, away up-stairs,
His mammy heerd him holler an' his daddy heerd him bawl,
An' when they turn't the kivvers down he wasn't there at all!
An' they seeked him in the rafter room an' cubby-hole an'
      press,
An' seeked him up the chimney-flue, an' everywheres, I guess,
But all they ever found was thist his pants an' round-about!—
An' the Gobble-uns'll git you
          Ef you
            Don't
              Watch
                Out!

An' one time a little girl 'ud allus laugh an' grin,
An' make fun of ever' one an' all her blood an' kin,
An' onct when they was "company," an' old folks was there,
She mocked 'em, an' shocked 'em, an' said she didn't care;
An' thist as she kicked her heels, an' turn't to run an' hide,
They was two great big Black Things a-standin' by her side,
An' they snatched her through the ceilin' 'fore she knowed
      what she's about!
An' the Gobble-uns'll git you
          Ef you
            Don't
              Watch
                Out!

An' little Orphant Annie says, when the blaze is blue
An' the lampwick sputters, an' the wind goes woo-oo!
An' you hear the crickets quit, an' the moon is gray,
An' the lightnin'-bugs in dew is all squenched away—

You better mind yer parents, an' yer teachers fond an' dear,
An' churish them 'at loves you, an' dry the orphant's tear,
An' he'p the pore an' needy ones 'at clusters all about,
Er the Gobble-uns'll git you

> Ef you
>> Don't
>>> Watch
>>>> Out!

From James Whitcomb Riley's " Rhymes of Childhood," copyright, 1890, by James Whitcomb Riley.

A Liz-Town Humorist

SETTIN' round the stove, last night,
Down at Wess's store, was me
And Mart Strimples, Tunk, and White,
And Doc Bills, and two er three
Fellers of the Mudsock tribe
No use tryin' to describe!
And says Doc, he says, says he—
"Talkin' 'bout good things to eat,
Ripe mushmillon's hard to beat!"

I chawed on. And Mart he 'lowed
Wortermillon beat the mush—
"Red," he says, "and juicy—Hush!—
I'll jes' leave it to the crowd!"
Then a Mudsock chap, says he—
"Punkin's good enough fer me—
Punkin pies, I mean," he says—
"Them beats millons! What say, Wess?"

I chawed on.   And Wess says—"Well,
You jes' fetch that wife of mine
All yer wortermillon-*rine*,
And she'll bile it down a spell—
In with sorgum, I suppose,
And what else, Lord only knows!—
But I'm here to tell all hands,
Them p'serves meets my demands!"

I chawed on.   And White he says—
"Well, I'll jes' stand in with Wess—
I'm no hog!"   And Tunk says—"I
Guess I'll pastur' out on pie
With the Mudsock boys!" says he;
"Now what's yourn?" he says to me:
I chawed on—fer quite a spell—
Then I speaks up, slow and dry—
"Jes' tobacker!" I-says-I—
And you'd orto' heerd 'em yell!

From James Whitcomb Riley's " Afterwhiles," copyright,
1887, 1888, by James Whitcomb Riley.

Albert Bigelow Paine

Mis' Smith

ALL day she hurried to get through,
The same as lots of wimmin do;
Sometimes at night her husban' said,
"Ma, ain't you goin' to come to bed?"
And then she'd kinder give a hitch,
And pause half way between a stitch,
And sorter sigh, and say that she
      Was ready as she'd ever be,
        She reckoned.

And so the years went one by one,
An' somehow she was never done;
An' when the angel said, as how
"Mis' Smith, it's time you rested now,"
She sorter raised her eyes to look
A second, as a stitch she took;
"All right, I'm comin' now," says she,
"I'm ready as I'll ever be,
        I reckon."

Sary "Fixes Up" Things

OH, yes, we've be'n fixin' up some sence we sold that piece o'
    groun'
Fer a place to put a golf-lynx to them crazy dudes from town.
(Anyway, they laughed like crazy when I had it specified,
Ef they put a golf-lynx on it, thet they'd haf to keep him tied.)

But they paid the price all reg'lar, an' then Sary says to me,
"Now we're goin' to fix the parlor up, an' settin'-room," says
    she.
Fer she 'lowed she'd been a-scrimpin' an' a-scrapin' all her life,
An' she meant fer once to have things good as Cousin Ed'ard's
    wife.

Well, we went down to the city, an' she bought the blamedest
    mess;
An' them clerks there must 'a' took her fer a' Astoroid, I guess;
Fer they showed her fancy bureaus which they said was shiffon-
    eers,
An' some more they said was dressers, an' some curtains called
    porteers.
An' she looked at that there furnicher, an' felt them curtains'
    heft;
Then she sailed in like a cyclone an' she bought 'em right an'
    left;
An' she picked a Bress'ls carpet thet was flowered like Cousin
    Ed's,
But she drawed the line com-pletely when we got to foldin'-beds.

Course, she said, 't'u'd make the parlor lots more roomier,
    she s'posed;
But she 'lowed she'd have a bedstid thet was shore to stay
    un-closed;
An' she stopped right there an' told us sev'ral tales of folks
    she'd read
Bein' overtook in slumber by the "fatal foldin'-bed."
"Not ef it wuz set in di'mon's! Nary foldin'-bed fer me!
I ain't goin' to start fer glory in a rabbit-trap!" says she.

"When the time comes I'll be ready an' a-waitin'; but ez yet,
I sha'n't go to sleep a-thinkin' that I've got the triggers set."

Well, sir, shore as yo' 're a-livin', after all thet Sary said,
'Fore we started home that evenin' she hed bought a foldin'-bed;
An' she's put it in the parlor, where it adds a heap o' style;
An' we're sleepin' in the settin'-room at present fer a while.
Sary still maintains it's han'some; an' them city folks'll see
That we're posted on the fashions when they visit us," says she;
But it plagues her some to tell her, ef it ain't no other use,
We can set it fer the golf-lynx ef he ever shud get loose.

Holman F. Day

Tale of the Kennebec Mariner

Guess I've never told you, sonny, of the strandin' and the
    wreck
Of the steamboat *Ezry Johnson* that run up the Kennebec.
That was 'fore the time of steam-cars, and the *Johnson* filled the
    bill
On the route between Augusty and the town of Waterville.

She was built old-fashioned model, with a bottom's flat's your
    palm,
With a paddle-wheel behind her, druv' by one great churnin'
    arm.
Couldn't say that she was speedy—sploshed along and made a
    touse,
But she couldn't go much faster than a man could tow a house.
Still, she skipped and skived tremendous, dodged the rocks
    and skun the shoals,
In a way the boats of these days couldn't do to save their souls.
Didn't draw no 'mount of water, went on top instead of through.
This is how there come to happen what I'm going to tell to *you*.
—Hain't no need to keep you guessing, for I know you won't
    suspect
How that thunderin' old *Ez. Johnson* ever happened to get
    wrecked.

She was overdue one ev'nin', fog come down most awful thick;
'Twas about like navigating round inside a feather tick.

Proper caper was to anchor, but she seemed to run all right,

And we humped her—though 'twas resky—kept her sloshing through the night.

Things went on all right till morning, but along 'bout half-past three

Ship went dizzy, blind, and crazy—waves seemed wust I ever see.

Up she went and down she scuttered; sometimes seemed to stand on end.

Then she'd wallopse, sideways, crossways, in a way, by gosh, to send

Shivers down your spine. She'd teeter, fetch a spring, and take a bounce,

Then squat down, sir, on her haunches with a most je-roosly jounce.

Folks got up and run a-screaming, forced the wheelhouse, grabbed at me,

—Thought we'd missed Augusty landin' and had gone plum out to sea.

—Fairly shot me full of questions, but I said 'twas jest a blow.

Still, that didn't seem to soothe 'em, for there warn't no wind, you know!

Yas, sir, spite of all that churnin', warn't a whisper of a breeze,

—No excuse for all that upset and those strange and dretful seas.

Couldn't spy a thing around us—every way 'twas pitchy black;

And I couldn't seem to comfort them poor critters on my back.

Couldn't give 'em information, for 'twas dark's a cellar shelf;

—Couldn't tell 'em nothing 'bout it—for I didn't know myself.

So I gripped the *Johnson's* tiller, kept the rudder riggin' taut,
Kept a-praying, chawed tobacker, give her steam, and let her
swat.
Now, my friend, jest listen stiddy: when the sun come out at
four
We warn't tossin' in the breakers off no stern and rock-bound
shore;
But I'd missed the gol-durned river, and I swow this 'ere is true,
I had sailed eight miles 'cross country in a heavy autumn dew.
There I was clear up in Sidney, and the tossings and the rolls
Simply happened 'cause we tackled sev'ral miles of cradle
knolls.
Sun come out and dried the dew out; there she was a stranded
wreck,
And they soaked me eighteen dollars' cartage to the Kennebec.

Cure for Homesickness

SHE wrote to her daddy in Portland, Maine, from out in Denver, Col.,
And she wrote, alas! despondently that life had commenced to
pall;
And this was a woful, woful case, for she was a six-months'
bride,
Who was won and wed in the State of Maine by the side of the
bounding tide.
And ah, alack, she was writing back, that she longed for Portland, Maine,
Till oh, her feelings had been that wrenched she could hardly
stand the strain!

15

Though her hubby dear was still sincere, she sighed the livelong
day

For a good old sniff of the sewers and salt from the breast of
Casco Bay.

And she wrote she sighed, and she said she'd cried, and her
appetite fell off,

And she'd grown as thin's a belaying pin, with a terrible
hacking cough;

And she sort of hinted that pretty soon she'd start on a reckless
scoot

And hook for her home in Portland, Maine, by the very shortest route.

But her daddy dear was a man of sense, and he handles fish
wholesale,

And he sat and fanned himself awhile with a big broad codfish
tail;

And he recollected the way he felt when he dwelt in the World's
Fair whirl,

He slapped his head. "By hake," he said, "I know what ails
that girl."

And he went to a ten-cord pile of cod and he pulled the biggest
out,

A jib-shaped critter, broad's a sail—three feet from tail to snout.

And he pasted a sheet of postage-stamps from snout clear down
to tail,

Put on a quick-delivery stamp, and sent the cod by mail.

She smelled it a-coming two blocks off on the top of the post-
man's pack;

She rushed to meet him, and scared him blind by climbing the
poor man's back.

But she got the fish, bit out a hunk, ate postage-stamps and all,

And a happy wife in a happy home lives out in Denver, Col.

Grampy Sings a Song

Row-DIDDY, dow de, my little sis,
Hush up your teasin' and listen to this:
'Tain't much of a jingle, 'tain't much of a tune,
But it's spang-fired truth about Chester Cahoon.
The thund'rinest fireman Lord ever made
Was Chester Cahoon of the Tuttsville Brigade.
He was boss of the tub and the foreman of hose;
When the 'larm rung he'd start, sis, a-sheddin' his clothes,
—Slung coat and slung wes'coat and kicked off his shoes,
A-runnin' like fun, for he'd no time to lose.
And he'd howl down the ro'd in a big cloud of dust,
For he made it his brag he was allus there fust.
—Allus there fust, with a whoop and a shout,
And he never shut up till the fire was out.
And he'd knock out the winders and save all the doors,
And tear off the clapboards, and rip up the floors,
For he allus allowed 'twas a tarnation sin
To 'low 'em to burn, for you'd want 'em agin.
He gen'rally stirred up the most of his touse
In hustling to save the outside of the house.
And after he'd wrassled and hollered and pried,
He'd let up and tackle the stuff 'twas inside.
To see him you'd think he was daft as a loon,
But that was just habit with Chester Cahoon.
Row diddy-iddy, my little sis,
Now see what ye think of a doin' like this:
The time of the fire at Jenkins' old place
It got a big start—was a desprit case;

17

The fambly they didn't know which way to turn.
And by gracious, it looked like it all was to burn.
But Chester Cahoon—oh, that Chester Cahoon,
He sailed to the roof like a reg'lar balloon;
Donno how he done it, but done it he did,
—Went down through the scuttle and shet down the lid.
And five minutes later that critter he came
To the second-floor winder surrounded by flame.
He lugged in his arms, sis, a stove and a bed,
And balanced a bureau right square on his head.
His hands they was loaded with crockery stuff,
China and glass; as if that warn't enough,
He'd rolls of big quilts round his neck like a wreath,
And carried Miss Jenkins' old aunt with his teeth.
You're right—gospel right, little sis—didn't seem
The critter'd get down, but he called for the stream,
And when it come strong and big round as my wrist,
He stuck out his legs, sis, and give 'em a twist;
And he hooked round the water jes' if 'twas a rope,
And down he come, easin' himself on the slope,
—So almighty spry that he made that 'ere stream
As fit for his pupp'us as if 'twas a beam.
Oh, the thund'rinest fireman Lord ever made
Was Chester Cahoon of the Tuttsville Brigade.

John W. Jones

A SORT of a double-breasted face had old John W. Jones,
Reddened and roughened by sun and wind, with angular high
cheek-bones.

Holman F. Day

At the fair, one time, of the Social Guild he received unique renown
By being elected unanimously the homeliest man in town.
The maidens giggled, the women smiled, the men laughed loud and long,
And old John W. leaned right back and ho-hawed good and strong.
And never was jest too broad for him—for all of the quip and chaff
That assailed his queer old mug through life he had but a hearty laugh.
"Ho, ho!" he'd snort, "Haw, haw!" he'd roar; "that's me, my friends, that's me!
Now hain't that the most skew-angled phiz that ever ye chanced to see?"
And then he would tell us this little tale. "'Twas one dark night," said he,
"I was driving along in a piece of woods, and there wasn't a ray to see,
And all to once my cart locked wheels with another old chap's cart;
We gee-ed and backed, but we hung there fast, and neither of us could start.
Then the stranger man he struck a match, to see how he'd git away,
And I vum, he had the homeliest face I've seen for many a day.
Wal, jest for a joke I grabbed his throat and pulled my pipe-case out,
And the stranger reckoned I had a gun, and he wrassled good and stout.

But I got him down on his back at last and straddled acrost his chest,

And allowed to him that he'd better plan to go to his last long rest.

He gasped and groaned he was poor and old and hadn't a blessed cent,

And almost blubbering asked to know what under the sun I meant.

Said I, 'I've sworn if I meet a man that's homelier'n what I be,

I'll kill him. I reckin I've got the man.' Says he, 'Please let me see?'

So I loosened a bit while he struck a match; he held it with trembling hand,

While through the tears in his poor old eyes my cross-piled face he scanned.

Then he dropped the match, and he groaned and said, 'If truly ye think that I

Am ha'f as homely as what you be, please shoot! I want to die.'"   *—" Pine Tree Ballads."*

The Ballad of Doc Pluff

DOCTOR PLUFF, who lived in Cornville, he was hearty, brisk, and bluff,

Didn't have much extry knowledge, but in some ways knowed enough;

Knowed enough to doctor hosses, cows an' dogs an' hens an' sheep;

When he come to doctor humans, wal, he wasn't quite so deep.

Holman F. Day

Still, he kind o' got ambitious, an' he went an' stubbed his toe
When he tried to tackle subjects that he really didn't know.

Doc he started out the fust-off as a vet'rinary doc,
An' he made a reputation jest as solid as a rock.
Doct'rin' hosses' throats, or such like, why, there warn't a man
    in town
Who could take a cone of paper, poof the sulphur furder down.
He could handle pips an' garget in a brisk an' thorough style,
An' there warn't a cow 'twould hook him when he give her
    castor ile.

As V. S. he had us solid, but he loosened up his hold
When he doctored Uncle Peaslee for his reg'lar April cold.
Uncle Peaslee allus caught it when he took his flannels off;
For a week or two he'd wheezle, sniff an' sneezle, bark an'
    cough;
An' at last, in desperation, when the thing became so tough,
He adopted some suggestions that were made by Doctor Pluff.

Fust o' March he started early, an' he reg'lar ev'ry day
From his heavy winter woolens tore a little strip away;
For the doc he had insisted that the change could thus be made,
'Cause the system wouldn't notice such an easy, steady grade.
Wal, sir, 'bout the last of April, Uncle Peaslee he had on
Jest the wris'ban's an' the collar—all the rest of it was gone.

Then—with Doctor Pluff advisin'—on a mild an' pleasant day
He took off the collar'n wris'ban's, and he throwed the things
    away;
An' in less'n thutty hours he was sudden tooken down
With the wust case of pneumony that we ever knowed in town

An' he dropped away in no time.   It was awful kind of rough,
An' we had our fust misgivin's 'bout the skill of old Doc Pluff.

Reckoned that 'ere scrape would down him an' he'd stick to
    hens an' cows,
But he'd got to be ambitious, an' he tackled Iral Howes.
Uncle Iral's kind o' feeble, but was bound to wean a ca'f;
Went to pull him off from suckin' when the critter'd had his
    ha'f.
Ca'f he turned around an' bunted—made him's mad's a tyke,
    ye see—
An' old Iral's leg was broken, little ways above the knee.
T'other doctor couldn't git there 'cause the goin' was so rough,
So they had to run their chances, an' they called on Doctor
    Pluff.

Doc he found old Iral groanin' where they'd laid him on the bed,
An' he took his old black finger, rolled up Iral's lip, an' said,
"Hay-teeth worn; can't chaw his vittles! Vittles therefore
    disagree;
It's as tough a case of colic as I think I ever see."
Some one started then to tell him, but the doc he had the floor,
An' he snapped 'em up so spiteful that they didn't say no more.

Then he wrinkled up his eyebrows, pursed his lips as tight's a
    bung,
Pried apart old Iral's grinders, an' says he, "Le's see your
    tongue."
"Why," says he, "I see the trouble—you've got garget of the
    blood,
An' if symptoms hain't deceivin', you have also lost your cud."

"Blame yer soul!" groaned Uncle Iral, "can't ye see what's
ailin' me?
That 'ere leg is broke!" "Oh, sartin," says the doc, "I see!
I see !"

Then he pulled off Iral's trousers, an' he spit upon his fist,
Grabbed that leg in good old earnest an' commenced to twist
an' twist.
Iral howled an' yowled an' fainted, then come to an' howled
some more,
He an' doc they fit an' wrassled on the bed an' on the floor.
Doc, though, held him to the wickin'—let old Iral howl an' beg,
Said he'd got to do his duty, straight'nin' out his blamed old
leg.

When the splints come off, though, later, wal, sir, Iral was
provoked;
Hain't surprised it made him ugly, for he sartainly was soaked.
Doc had set it so the knee-joint comes behind, jest like a cow's,
An' 'twould make ye die a-laughin', would that gait of Iral
Howes'.
If that case of Uncle Peaslee wasn't damagin' enough,
Bet your life that job on Iral made us shy of old Doc Pluff.
—"*Pine Tree Ballads.*"

A Settin' Hen

When a hen is bound to set,
Seems as though 'tain't etiket
Dowsin' her in water till
She's connected with a chill.

Seems as though 'twas skursely right
Givin' her a dreadful fright,
Tyin' rags around her tail,
Poundin' on an old tin pail,
Chasin' her around the yard.
Seems as though 'twas kind of hard
Bein' kicked and slammed and shooed
'Cause she wants to raise a brood.
I sh'd say it's gettin' gay
Jest 'cause natur' wants its way.
While ago my neighbor, Penn,
Started bustin' up a hen;
Went to yank her off the nest;
Hen, though, made a peck, and jest
Grabbed his thumb-nail good and stout,
Almost yanked the darn thing out.
Penn he twitched away and then,
Tried again to grab that hen.
But, by ginger! she had spunk,
'Cause she took and nipped a hunk
Big's a bean right out his palm,
Swallered it, and cool and calm
H'isted up and yelled "Cah-dah—"
Sounded like she said "Hoo-rah!"
Wal, sir, when that hen done that,
Penn he bowed, took off his hat,
Spunk jest suits him, you can bet:
"Set," says he, "gol darn ye, SET!"

—" *Pine Tree Ballads*."

Frank Gelett Burgess

The Bohemians of Boston

THE "Orchids" were as tough a crowd
As Boston anywhere allowed;
It was a club of wicked men—
The oldest, twelve, the youngest, ten;
They drank their soda colored green,
They talked of "Art," and "Philistine,"
They wore buff "wescoats," and their hair
It used to make the waiters stare!
They were so shockingly behaved
And Boston thought them *so* depraved,
Policemen, stationed at the door,
Would raid them every hour or more!
They used to smoke (!) and laugh out loud (!)
They were a very devilish crowd!
They formed a Cult, far subtler, brainier,
Than ordinary Anglomania,
For all as Jacobites were reckoned,
And gaily toasted Charles the Second!
(What would the Bonnie Charlie say,
If he could see that crowd to-day?)
Fitz-Willieboy McFlubadub
Was Regent of the Orchid's Club;
A wild Bohemian was he,
And spent his money fast and free.
He thought no more of spending dimes
On some debauch of pickled limes,

Than you would think of spending nickels
To buy a pint of German pickles!
The Boston maiden passed him by
With sidelong glances of her eye,
She dared not speak (he *was* so wild),
Yet worshiped this Lotharian child.
Fitz-Willieboy was so *blasé*,
He burned a *Transcript* up one day!
The Orchids fashioned all their styles
On Flubadub's infernal guile.
That awful Boston oath was his—
He used to 'jaculate, "Gee Whiz!"
He showed them that immoral haunt,
The dirty Chinese Restaurant,
And there they'd find him, even when
It got to be as late as ten!
He ate chopped *suey* (with a fork).
You should have heard the villain talk
Of one *reporter* that he knew (!)
An artist, and an actor, too!!!
The Orchids went from bad to worse,
Made epigrams—attempted verse!
Boston was horrified and shocked
To hear the way those Orchids mocked;
For they made fun of Boston ways,
And called good men Provincial Jays!
The end must come to such a story,
Gone is the wicked Orchid's glory,
The room was raided by the police,
One night, for breaches of the Peace
(There had been laughter, long and loud,
In Boston this is not allowed),

Frank Gelett Burgess

And there, the sergeant of the squad
Found awful evidence—my God!—
Fitz-Willieboy McFlubadub,
The Regent of the Orchid's Club,
Had written on the window-sill,
This shocking outrage—"Beacon H—ll!"
　　　　—"*The Burgess Nonsense Book.*"

George Ade

The Fable of the Preacher who Flew his Kite, but not Because he Wished to Do so

A CERTAIN preacher became wise to the Fact that he was not making a Hit with his Congregation. The Parishioners did not seem inclined to seek him out after Services and tell him he was a Pansy. He suspected that they were Rapping him on the Quiet.

The Preacher knew there must be something wrong with his Talk. He had been trying to Expound in a clear and straightforward Manner, omitting Foreign Quotations, setting up for illustration of his Points such Historical Characters as were familiar to his hearers, putting the stubby Old English words ahead of the Latin, and rather flying low along the Intellectual Plane of the Aggregation that chipped in to pay his Salary.

But the Pewholders were not tickled. They could Understand everything he said, and they began to think he was Common.

So he studied the Situation and decided that if he wanted to Win them and make everybody believe he was a Nobby and Boss Minister he would have to hand out a little Guff. He fixed it up Good and Plenty.

On the following Sunday Morning he got up in the Lookout and read a text that didn't mean anything, read from either Direction, and then he sized up his Flock with a Dreamy Eye and said: "We cannot more adequately voice the Poetry and

George Ade

Mysticism of our Text than in those familiar Lines of the great Icelandic Poet, Ikon Navrojk:

> " 'To hold is not to have—
> Under the seared Firmament,
> Where Chaos sweeps, and vast Futurity
> Sneers at these puny Aspirations—
> There is the full Reprisal.' "

When the Preacher concluded this Extract from the Well-Known Icelandic Poet he paused and looked downward, breathing heavily through his Nose, like Camille in the Third Act.

A stout Woman in the Front Row put on her Eyeglasses and leaned forward so as not to miss Anything. A Venerable Harness-Dealer over at the Right nodded his Head solemnly. He seemed to recognize the Quotation. Members of the Congregation glanced at one another as if to say, "This is certainly Hot Stuff!"

The Preacher wiped his Brow and said he had no Doubt that every one within the Sound of his Voice remembered what Quarolius had said, following the same Line of Thought. It was Quarolius who disputed the Contention of the great Persian Theologian Ramtazuk, that the soul in its reaching out after the Unknowable was guided by the Spiritual Genesis of Motive rather than by Mere Impulse of Mentality. The Preacher didn't know what all this meant, and he didn't care, but you can rest easy that the Pewholders were On in a minute. He talked off in just the Way that Cyrano talks when he gets Roxane so Dizzy that she nearly falls off the Piazza.

The Parishioners bit their Lower Lips and hungered for more First-Class Language. They had paid their Money for

Tall Talk and were prepared to solve any and all Styles of Delivery. They held on to the Cushions and seemed to be having a Nice Time.

The Preacher quoted copiously from the Great Poet, Amebius. He recited eighteen lines of Greek and then said, "How true this is!" And not a Parishioner batted an Eye.

It was Amebius whose Immortal Lines he recited in order to prove the Extreme Error of the Position assumed in the Controversy by the Famous Italian, Polenta.

He had them Going, and there wasn't a Thing to it. When he would get tired of faking Philosophy he would quote from a Celebrated Poet of Ecuador or Tasmania or some other Seaport Town. Compared with this Verse, all of which was of the same School as the Icelandic Masterpiece, the most obscure and clouded Passage in Robert Browning was like a Plate-Glass Front in a State Street Candy Store just after the Colored Boy gets through using the Chamois.

After that he became Eloquent, and began to get rid of long Boston Words that hadn't been used before that Season. He grabbed a rhetorical Roman Candle in each Hand and you couldn't see him for the Sparks.

After which he sunk his Voice to a Whisper and talked about the Birds and the Flowers. Then, although there was no Cue for him to Weep, he shed a few real Tears. And there wasn't a dry Glove in the Church.

After he sat down he could tell by the Scared Look of the People in Front that he had made a Ten-Strike.

Did they give him the Joyous Palm that Day? Sure!

The Stout Lady could not control her Feelings when she told how much the Sermon had helped her. The venerable Harness-Dealer said he wished to indorse the Able and Scholarly Criticism of Polenta.

George Ade

In fact, every one said the Sermon was Superfine and Dandy. The only thing that worried the Congregation was the Fear that if it wished to retain such a Whale it might have to Boost his Salary.

In the Meantime the Preacher waited for some one to come and ask about Polenta, Amebius, Ramtazuk, Quarolius and the great Icelandic Poet, Novrojk. But no one had the Face to step up and confess his Ignorance of these Celebrities. The Pewholders didn't even admit among themselves that the Preacher had rung in some New Ones. They stood Pat, and merely said it was an Elegant Sermon.

Perceiving that they would stand for Anything, the Preacher knew what to do after that.

MORAL.—*Give the People what they Think they want.*
—"Fables In Slang."

The Fable of the Caddy who Hurt his Head While Thinking

ONE day a Caddy sat in the Long Grass near the Ninth Hole and wondered if he had a Soul. His number was 27, and he almost had forgotten his Real Name.

As he sat and Meditated, two Players passed him. They were going the Long Round, and the Frenzy was upon them.

They followed the Gutta-Percha Balls with the intent swiftness of trained Bird-Dogs, and each talked feverishly of Brassy Lies, and getting past the Bunker, and Lofting to the Green, and Slicing into the Bramble—each telling his own Game to the Ambient Air, and ignoring what the other Fellow had to say.

As they did the St. Andrews Full Swing for eighty Yards apiece and then Followed Through with the usual Explanations of how it Happened, the Caddy looked at them and Reflected that they were much inferior to his Father.

His Father was too Serious a Man to get out in Mardi Gras Clothes and hammer a Ball from one Red flag to another.

His Father worked in a Lumber-Yard.

He was an Earnest Citizen, who seldom Smiled, and he knew all about the Silver Question and how J. Pierpont Morgan done up a Free People on the Bond Issue.

The Caddy wondered why it was that his Father, a really Great Man, had to shove Lumber all day and could seldom get one Dollar to rub against another, while these superficial Johnnies who played Golf all the Time had Money to Throw at the Birds. The more he Thought the more his Head ached.

MORAL.—*Don't try to Account for Anything.*

The Fable of the Two Mandolin Players and the Willing Performer

A VERY attractive Debutante knew two young Men who called on her every Thursday Evening and brought their Mandolins along.

They were Conventional Young Men, of the Kind that you see wearing Spring Overcoats in the Clothing Advertisements. One was named Fred and the other was Eustace.

The Mothers of the Neighborhood often remarked, "What Perfect Manners Fred and Eustace have!" Merely as an aside, it may be added that Fred and Eustace were more Popular with the Mothers than they were with the Younger Set, although no one could say a Word against either of them. Only, it was rumored in Keen Society that they didn't Belong. The fact

George Ade

that they went Calling in a Crowd, and took their Mandolins along, may give the Acute Reader some Idea of the Life that Fred and Eustace held out to the Young Women of their Acquaintance.

The Debutante's name was Myrtle. Her Parents were very Watchful, and did not encourage her to receive Callers, except such as were known to be Exemplary Young Men. Fred and Eustace were a few of those who escaped the Black List. Myrtle always appeared to be glad to see them, and they regarded her as a Darned Swell Girl.

Fred's Cousin came from St. Paul on a Visit; and one Day, in the Street, he saw Myrtle, and noticed that Fred tipped his Hat, and gave her a Stage Smile.

"Oh, Queen of Sheba!" exclaimed the Cousin from St. Paul, whose name was Gus, as he stood stock still and watched Myrtle's Reversible Plaid disappear around a Corner. "She's a Bird. Do you know her well?"

"I know her Quite Well," replied Fred coldly. "She is a Charming Girl."

"She is all of that. You're a great Describer. And now what Night are you going to take me around to Call on her?"

Fred very naturally Hemmed and Hawed. It must be remembered that Myrtle was a member of an Excellent Family, and had been schooled in the Proprieties, and it was not to be supposed that she would crave the Society of slangy old Gus, who had an abounding Nerve, and furthermore was as Fresh as the Mountain-Air.

He was the Kind of Fellow who would see a Girl twice, and then, upon meeting her the Third Time, he would go up and straighten her Cravat for her and call her by her First Name.

Put him into a Strange Company—en route to a Picnic—and by the time the Baskets were unpacked he would have a

Blonde all to himself, and she would have traded her Fan for his College-Pin.

If a Fair-Looker on the Street happened to glance at him Hard he would run up and seize her by the Hand and convince her that they had Met. And he always Got Away with it too.

In a Department Store, while waiting for the Cash-Boy to come back with the Change, he would find out the Girl's Name, her Favorite Flower, and where a Letter would reach her.

Upon entering a Parlor-Car at St. Paul he would select a Chair next to the Most Promising One in Sight, and ask her if she cared to have the Shade lowered.

Before the Train cleared the Yards he would have the Porter bringing a Footstool for the Lady.

At Hastings he would be asking her if she wanted Something to Read.

At Red Wing he would be telling her that she resembled Maxine Elliott, and showing her his Watch, left to him by his Grandfather, a Prominent Virginian.

At La Crosse he would be reading the Menu Card to her, and telling her how different it is when you have Some One to join you in a Bite.

At Milwaukee he would go out and buy a Bouquet for her, and when they rode into Chicago they would be looking out of the same Window, and he would be arranging for her Baggage with the Transfer Man. After that they would be Old Friends.

Now, Fred and Eustace had been at School with Gus, and they had seen his Work, and they were not disposed to Introduce him into One of the most Exclusive Homes in the City.

They had known Myrtle for many Years; but they did not dare to Address her by her First Name, and they were Positive that if Gus attempted any of his usual Tactics with her she would be Offended; and, naturally enough, they would be Blamed for bringing him to the House.

But Gus insisted. He said he had seen Myrtle, and she Suited him from the Ground up, and he proposed to have Friendly Doings with her. At last they told him they would take him if he promised to Behave. Fred warned him that Myrtle would frown down any Attempt to be Familiar on Short Acquaintance, and Eustace said that as long as he had known Myrtle he had never Presumed to be Free and Forward with her. He had simply played the Mandolin. That was as Far Along as he had ever got.

Gus told them not to Worry about him. All he asked was a Start. He said he was a Willing Performer, but as yet he never had been Disqualified for Crowding. Fred and Eustace took this to mean that he would not Overplay his Attentions, so they escorted him to the House.

As soon as he had been Presented, Gus showed her where to sit on the Sofa, then he placed himself about Six Inches away and began to Buzz, looking her straight in the Eye. He said that when he first saw her he Mistook her for Miss Prentice, who was said to be the Most Beautiful Girl in St. Paul, only, when he came closer, he saw that it couldn't be Miss Prentice, because Miss Prentice didn't have such Lovely Hair. Then he asked her the Month of her Birth and told her Fortune, thereby coming nearer to Holding her Hand within Eight Minutes than Eustace had come in a Lifetime.

"Play something, Boys," he Ordered, just as if he had paid them Money to come along and make Music for him.

They unlimbered their Mandolins and began to play a Sousa March. He asked Myrtle if she had seen the New Moon. She replied that she had not, so they went Outside.

When Fred and Eustace finished the first Piece, Gus appeared at the open Window and asked them to play "The Georgia Camp-Meeting," which had always been one of his Favorites.

So they played that, and when they had Concluded there came a Voice from the Outer Darkness, and it was the Voice of Myrtle. She said, "I'll tell you what to Play; play the 'Intermezzo.'"

Fred and Eustace exchanged Glances. They began to Perceive that they had been backed into a Siding. With a few Potted Palms in front of them, and two cards from the Union, they would have been just the same as a Hired Orchestra.

But they played the "Intermezzo" and felt Peevish. Then they went to the Window and looked out. Gus and Myrtle were sitting in the Hammock, which had quite a Pitch toward the Center. Gus had braced himself by Holding to the back of the Hammock. He did not have his Arm around Myrtle, but he had it Extended in a Line parallel with her Back. What he had done wouldn't Justify a Girl in saying "Sir!" but it started a Real Scandal with Fred and Eustace. They saw that the only Way to Get Even with her was to go Home without saying "Good Night."

So they slipped out the Side Door, shivering with Indignation.

After that, for several Weeks, Gus kept Myrtle so Busy that she had no Time to think of considering other Candidates. He sent Books to her Mother, and allowed the Old Gentleman to take Chips away from him at Poker.

They were married in the Autumn, and Father-in-Law took Gus into the Firm, saying that he had needed a good Pusher for a Long Time.

At the Wedding the two Mandolin Players were permitted to act as Ushers.

MORAL.—*To get a fair Trial of Speed, use a Pace-Maker.*

—"Girl Proposition."

F. P. Dunne—"Mr. Dooley"

On Gold-Seeking

"WELL, sir," said Mr. Hennessy, "that Alaska's th' gr-reat place. I thought 'twas nawthin' but an iceberg with a few seals roostin' on it, an' wan or two hundhred Ohio politicians that can't be killed on account iv th' threaty iv Pawrs. But here they tell me 'tis fairly smothered in goold. A man stubs his toe on th' ground an lifts th' top off iv a goold mine. Ye go to bed at night an' wake up with goold fillin' in ye'er teeth."

"Yes," said Mr. Dooley. "Clancy's son was in here this mornin', an' he says a frind iv his wint to sleep out in th' open wan night, an' whin he got up his pants assayed four ounces iv goold to th' pound, an' his whiskers panned out as much as thirty dollars net."

"If I was a young man an' not tied down here," said Mr. Hennessy, "I'd go there; I wud go."

"I wud not," said Mr. Dooley. "Whin I was a young man in th' ol' counthry, we heerd th' same story about all America. We used to set be th' tur-rf fire o' nights, kickin' our bare legs on th' flure an' wishin' we was in New York, where all ye had to do was to hold ye'er hat an' th' goold guineas'd dhrop into it. An' whin I got to be a man, I come over here with a ham and a bag iv oatmeal, as sure that I'd return in a year with money enough to dhrive me own ca-ar as I was that me name was Martin Dooley. An' that was a cinch.

"But, faith, whin I'd been here a week, I seen that there was nawthin' but mud undher th' pavement—I learned that be means iv a pick-ax at tin shillin's th' day—an' that, though

37

there was plenty iv goold, thim that had it were froze to it; an'
I come West, still lookin' f'r mines. Th' on'y mine I sthruck
at Pittsburg was a hole f'r sewer-pipe. I made it. Siven
shillin's th' day. Smaller thin New York, but th' livin' was
cheaper, with Mon'gahela rye five a throw, put ye'er hand
around th' glass.

"I was still dreamin' goold, an' I wint down to Saint Looey.
Th' nearest I come to a fortune there was findin' a quarther on
th' sthreet as I leaned over th' dashboord iv a car to whack th'
off mule. Whin I got to Chicago, I looked around f'r the goold
mine. They was Injuns here thin. But they wasn't anny
mines I cud see. They was mud to be shoveled an' dhrays
to be dhruv an' beats to be walked. I choose th' dhray; f'r
I was niver cut out f'r a copper, an' I'd had me fill iv excavatin'.
An' I dhruv th' dhray till I wint into business.

"Me experyence with goold minin' is it's always in th' nex'
county. If I was to go to Alaska, they'd tell me iv th' finds in
Seeberya. So I think I'll stay here. I'm a silver man, annyhow; an' I'm contint if I can see goold wanst a year, whin some
prominent citizen smiles over his newspaper. I'm thinkin'
that ivry man has a goold mine undher his own durestep or in
his neighbor's pocket at th' farthest."

"Well, annyhow," said Mr. Hennessy, "I'd like to kick up
th' sod an' find a ton iv goold undher me fut."

"What wud ye do if ye found it?" demanded Mr. Dooley.

"I—I dinnaw," said Mr. Hennessy, whose dreaming had
not gone this far. Then, recovering himself, he exclaimed
with great enthusiasm, "I'd throw up me job an'—an' live like
a prince."

"I tell ye what ye'd do," said Mr. Dooley. "Ye'd come
back here an' sthrut up an' down th' sthreet with ye'er thumbs
in ye'er armpits; an' ye'd dhrink too much, an' ride in sthreet

ca-ars. Thin ye'd buy foldin' beds an' piannies, an' start a reel-estate office. Ye'd be fooled a good deal an' lose a lot iv ye'er money, an' thin ye'd tighten up. Ye'd be in a cold fear night an' day that ye'd lose ye'er fortune. Ye'd wake up in th' middle iv th' night, dhreamin' that ye was back at th' gas-house with ye'er money gone. Ye'd be prisidint iv a charitable society. Ye'd have to wear ye'er shoes in th' house, an' ye'er wife'd have ye around to rayciptions an' dances. Ye'd move to Mitchigan Avnoo, an' ye'd hire a coachman that'd laugh at ye. Ye'er boys'd be joods an' ashamed iv ye, an' ye'd support ye'er daughters' husbands. Ye'd rackrint ye'er tinants an' lie about ye'er taxes. Ye'd go back to Ireland an' put on airs with ye'er cousin Mike. Ye'd be a mane, onscrupulous ol' cur-mudgeon; an', whin ye'd die, it'd take half ye'er fortune f'r rayqueems to put ye r-right. I don't want ye iver to speak to me whin ye get rich, Hinnissy."

"I won't," said Mr. Hennessy.

—*"Mr. Dooley on Peace and in War."*

On Expert Testimony

"ANNYTHING new?" said Mr. Hennessy, who had been wait-ing patiently for Mr. Dooley to put down his newspaper.

"I've been r-readin' th' tistimony iv th' Lootgert case," said Mr. Dooley.

"What d'ye think iv it?"

"I think so," said Mr. Dooley.

"Think what?"

"How do I know?" said Mr. Dooley. "How do I know what I think? I'm no combination iv chemist, doctor, oste-ologist, polisman, an' sausage-maker, that I can give ye an opinion right off th' bat. A man needs to be all iv thim things to detarmine annything about a murdher trile in these days. This shows how intilligent our methods is, as Hogan says. A large German man is charged with puttin' his wife away into a breakfas'-dish, an' he says he didn't do it. Th' question thin is, Did or did not Alphonse Lootgert stick Mrs. L. into a vat, an' rayjooce her to a quick lunch? Am I right?"

"Ye ar-re," said Mr. Hennessy.

"That's simple enough. What th' Coort ought to've done was to call him up, an' say: 'Lootgert, where's ye'er good woman?' If Lootgert cudden't tell, he ought to be hanged on gin'ral principles; f'r a man must keep his wife around th' house, an' whin she isn't there it shows he's a poor provider. But, if Lootgert says, 'I don't know where me wife is,' the Coort shud say: 'Go out an' find her. If ye can't projooce her in a week, I'll fix ye.' An' let that be th' end iv it.

"But what do they do? They get Lootgert into coort an' stand him up befure a gang iv young rayporthers an' th' likes iv thim to make pitchers iv him. Thin they summon a jury composed iv poor tired, sleepy expressmen an' tailors an' clerks. Thin they call in a profissor from a colledge. 'Professor,' says th' lawyer f'r the State, 'I put it to ye if a wooden vat three hundherd an' sixty feet long, twenty-eight feet deep, an' sivinty-five feet wide, an' if three hundherd pounds iv caustic soda boiled, an' if the leg iv a guinea-pig, an' ye said yestherdah about bi-carbonate iv soda, an' if it washes up an' washes over, an' th' slimy, slippery stuff, an' if a false tooth or a lock iv hair or a jawbone or a goluf ball across th' cellar eleven feet nine inches—that is, two inches this way an' five gallons that?' 'I agree with ye intirely,' says th' profissor. 'I made lab'ratory experiments in an' ir'n basin, with bichloride iv gool, which I will call soup-stock, an' coal-tar, which I will call

ir'n filings. I mixed th' two over a hot fire, an' left in a cool
place to harden. I thin packed it in ice, which I will call glue,
an' rock-salt, which I will call fried eggs, an' obtained a dark,
queer solution that is a cure f'r freckles, which I will call
antimony or doughnuts or annything I blamed please.'

"'But,' says th' lawyer f'r th' State, 'measurin' th' vat with
gas—an' I lave it to ye whether this is not th' on'y fair test—
an' supposin' that two feet acrost is akel to tin feet sideways,
an' supposin' that a thick green an' hard substance, an' I dare-
say it wud; an' supposin' you may, takin' into account th' meas-
uremints—twelve be eight—th' vat bein' wound with twine
six inches fr'm th' handle an' a rub iv th' green, thin ar-re not
human teeth often found in counthry sausage?' 'In th' winter,'
says th' profissor. 'But th' sisymoid bone is sometimes seen
in th' fut, sometimes worn as a watch-charm. I took two
sisymoid bones, which I will call poker dice, an' shook thim
together in a cylinder, which I will call Fido, poored in a can
iv milk, which I will call gum arabic, took two pounds iv rough-
on-rats, which I rayfuse to call; but th' raysult is th' same.'
Question be th' Coort: 'Different?' Answer: 'Yis.' Th'
Coort: 'Th' same.' Be Misther McEwen: 'Whose bones?'
Answer: 'Yis.' Be Misther Vincent: 'Will ye go to th'
divvle?' Answer: 'It dissolves th' hair.'

"Now what I want to know is where th' jury gets off. What
has that collection iv pure-minded pathrites to larn fr'm this
here polite discussion, where no wan is so crool as to ask what
anny wan else means? Thank th' Lord, whin th' case is all
over, the jury'll pitch th' tistimony out iv th' window, an' consider three questions: 'Did Lootgert look as though he'd kill
his wife? Did his wife look as though she ought so be kilt?
Isn't it time we wint to supper?' An', howiver they answer,
they'll be right, an' it'll make little diff'rence wan way or

th' other. Th' German vote is too large an' ignorant, annyhow."—"*Mr. Dooley on Peace and in War.*"

Home Life of Geniuses

"A WOMAN ought to be careful who she marries," said Mr. Dooley.

"So ought a man," said Mr. Hennessy, with feeling.

"It don't make so much diff'rence about him," said Mr. Dooley. "Whin a man's marrid he's a marrid man. That's all ye can say about him. Iv coorse, he thinks marredge is goin' to change th' whole current iv his bein', as Hogan says. But it doesn't. Afther he's been hooked up f'r a few months he finds he was marrid befure, even if he wasn't, which is often th' case, d'ye mind. Th' first bride iv his bosom was th' Day's Wurruk, an' it can't be put off. They'se no groun's f'r dissolvin' that marredge, Hinnissy. Ye can't say to th' Day's Wurruk: 'Here, take this bunch iv alimony an' go on th' stage.' It turns up at breakfast about th' fourth month afther th' weddin' an' creates a scandal. Th' unforchnit man thries to shoo it off, but it fixes him with its eye an' hauls him away fr'm the bacon an' eggs, while the lady opposite weeps an' wondhers what he can see in annything so old an' homely. It says, 'Come with me, aroon,' an' he goes. An' afther that he spinds most iv his time an' often a good deal iv his money with th' enchantress. I tell ye what, Hinnissy, th' Day's Wurruk has broke up more happy homes thin comic opry. If th' coorts wud allow it, manny a woman cud get a divorce on th' groun's that her husband cared more f'r his Day's Wurruk thin he did f'r her. 'Hinnissy varsus Hinnissy; corryspondint, th' Day's Wurruk.' They'd be ividence that th' defendant was seen ridin' in a cab with th' corryspondint, that he took it to a picnic, that he wint to th' theayter with it, that he talked about it in his sleep, an' that, lost to all sinse iv shame, he even escoorted it home with him an' inthrajooced it to his varchoos wife an' innocint childher. So it don't make much diff'rence who a man marries. If he has a job, he's safe.

"But with a woman 'tis diff'rent. Th' man puts down on'y part iv th' bet. Whin he's had enough iv th' conversation that in Union Park undher th' threes med him think he was talkin' with an intellechool joyntess, all he has to do is put on his coat, grab up his dinner-pail an' go down to th' shops, to be happy though marrid. But a woman, I tell ye, bets all she has. A man don't have to marry, but a woman does. Ol' maids an' clargymen do th' most good in th' wurruld an' we love thim f'r th' good they do. But people, especially women, don't want to be loved that way. They want to be loved because people can't help lovin' thim no matther how bad they are. Th' story books that ye give ye'er daughter Honoria all tell her 'tis just as good not to be married. She reads about how kind Dorothy was to Lulu's childher an' she knows Dorothy was th' betther woman, but she wants to be Lulu. Her heart, an' a cold look in th' eye iv th' wurruld an' her Ma tell her to hurry up. Arly in life she looks f'r th' man iv her choice in th' tennis records; later she reads th' news fr'm th' militia encampment; thin she studies th' socyal raygisther; further on she makes hersilf familyar with Bradsthreet's rayports, an' fin'lly she watches th' place where life-presarvers are hangin'.

"Now, what kind iv a man ought a woman to marry? She oughtn't to marry a young man, because she'll grow old quicker thin he will; she oughtn't to marry an old man, because he'll be much older befure he's younger; she oughtn't to marry a poor man, because he may become rich an' lose her; she oughtn't to marry a rich man, because if he becomes poor she can't lose him; she oughtn't to marry a man that knows more thin she does, because he'll niver fail to show it, an' she oughtn't to marry a man that knows less, because he may niver catch up. But, above all things, she mustn't marry a janius. A flurewalker, perhaps; a janius niver.

"I tell ye this because I've been r-readin' a book Hogan give me, about th' divvle's own time a janius had with his fam'ly. A cap iv industhry may have throuble in his family till there isn't a whole piece iv chiny in th' cupboard, an' no wan will be the wiser f'r it but th' hired girl an' th' doctor that paints th' black eye. But ivrybody knows what happens in a janius's house. Th' janius always tells th' bartinder. Besides, he has other janiuses callin' on him an' 'tis th' business iv a janius to write about th' domestic throubles iv other janiuses so posterity'll know what a hard thing it is to be a janius. I've been readin' this book iv Hogan's, an' as I tell ye, 'tis about th' misery a wretched woman inflicted on a pote's life.

"'Our hayro,' says th' author, 'at this peeryod conthracted an unforchnit alliance that was destined to cast a deep gloom over his career. At th' age iv fifty, afther a life devoted to the pursoot iv such gaiety as janiuses have always found niciss'ry to solace their avenin's, he married a young an' beautiful girl some thirty-two years his junior. This wretched crather had no appreciation iv lithrachoor or lithry men. She was frivolous an' light-minded an' ividently considhered that nawthin' was rally lithrachoor that cudden't be translated into groceries. Niver shall I f'rget th' expression iv despair on th' face iv this godlike man as he came into Casey's saloon wan starry July avenin' an' staggered into his familyar seat, holdin' in his hand a bit iv soiled paper which he tore into fragmints an' hurled into the coal-scuttle. On that crumpled parchmint findin' a

44

somber grave among th' disinterred relics iv an age long past, to wit, th' cariboniferious or coal age, was written th' iver-mim'rable pome: "Ode to Gin." Our frind had scribbled it hastily at th' dinner iv th' Betther-thin-Shakespeare Club, an' had attimpted to read it to his wife through th' keyhole iv her bed-room dure an' met no response fr'm th' fillystein but a pitcher iv wather through th' thransom. Forchnitly he had presarved a copy on his cuff an' th' gem was not lost to posterity. But such was th' home life iv wan iv th' gr-reatest iv lithry masters, a man indowed be nachure with all that shud make a woman adore him as is proved be his tindher varses: "To Carrie," "To Maude," "To Flossie," "To Angebel," "To Queenie," an' so foorth. De Bonipoort in his cillybrated "Mimores," in which he tells ivrything unpleasant he see or heerd in his frinds' houses, gives a sthrikin' pitcher iv a scene that happened befure his eyes. "Afther a few basins iv absceenthe in th' reev gosh," says he, "Parnassy invited us home to dinner. Sivral iv th' bum vivonts was hard to wake up, but fin'lly we arrived at th' handsome cellar where our gr-reat frind had installed his un-worthy fam'ly. Ivrything pinted to th' admirable taste iv th' thrue artist. Th' tub, th' washboard, th' biler singin' on th' fire, th' neighbor's washin' dancin' on the clothes-rack, were all in keepin' with th' best ideels iv what a pote's home shud be. Th' wife, a faded but still pretty woman, welcomed us more or less, an' with th' assistance iv sivral bottles iv paint we had brought with us we was soon launched on a feast iv raison an' a flow iv soul. Unhappily befure th' raypast was con-cluded a mis'rable scene took place. Amid cries iv approval, Parnassy read his mim'rable pome intitled: 'I wisht I nivir got marrid.' Afther finishin' in a perfect roar iv applause, he happened to look up an' see his wife callously rockin' th' baby. With th' impetchosity so charackteristic iv th' man, he broke a soup-plate over her head an' burst into tears on th' flure, where gentle sleep soon soothed th' pangs iv a weary heart. We left as quietly as as we cud, considherin' th' way th' chairs was placed, an' wanst undher th' stars comminted on th' ir'ny iv fate that condimned so great a man to so milancholy a distiny."

"'This,' says our author, 'was th' daily life iv th' hayro f'r tin years. In what purgatory will that infamous woman suffer if Hiven thinks as much iv janiuses as we think iv oursilves. Forchnitly th' pote was soon to be marcifully relieved. He left her an' she married a boorjawce with whom she led a life iv coarse happiness. It is sad to relate that some years aftherward th' great pote, havin' called to make a short touch on th' woman f'r whom he had sacryficed so much, was unfeelingly kicked out iv th' boorjawce's plumbin' shop.'

"So, ye see, Hinnissy, why a woman oughtn't to marry a janius. She can't be cross or peevish or angry or jealous or frivolous or annything else a woman ought to be at times f'r fear it will get into th' ditchn'ry iv biography, an' she'll go down to histhry as a termygant. A termygant, Hinnissy, is a woman who's heerd talkin' to her husband after they've been marrid a year. Hogan says all janiuses was unhappily marrid. I guess that's thrue iv their wives too. He says if ye hear iv a pote who got on with his fam'ly, scratch him fr'm ye'er public lib'ry list. An' there ye ar-re."

"Ye know a lot about marredge," said Mr. Hennessy.

"I do," said Mr. Dooley.

"Ye was niver marrid?"

"No," said Mr. Dooley. "No, I say, givin' three cheers. I know about marredge th' way an asthronomer knows about th' stars. I'm studyin' it through me glass all the time."

"Ye're an asthronomer," said Mr. Hennessy; "but," he added, tapping himself lightly on the chest, "I'm a star."

F. P. Dunne

"Go home," said Mr. Dooley crossly, "befure th' mornin' comes to put ye out."—"*Mr. Dooley's Opinions.*"

The City as a Summer Resort

"WHERE'S Dorsey, the plumber, these days?" asked Mr. Hennessy.

"Haven't ye heerd?" said Mr. Dooley. "Dorsey's become a counthry squire. He's landed gintry, like me folks in th' ol' dart. He lives out among th' bur-rds an' th' bugs, in a house that looks like a cuckoo clock. In an hour or two ye'll see him go by to catch the five five. He won't catch it because there ain't anny five five. Th' la-ad that makes up th' time-table found las' week that if he didn't get away earlier he cudden't take his girl f'r a buggy ride, an' he's changed th' five five to four forty-eight. Dorsey will wait f'r th' six siven an' he'll find that it don't stop at Paradise Manor, where he lives on Satur-dahs an' Winsdahs except Fridahs in Lent. He'll get home at ilivin o'clock, an' if his wife's f'rgot to lave th' lanthern in th' deepo he'll crawl up to th' house on his hands an' knees. I see him las' night in at th' dhrug sthore buyin' ile iv peppermint f'r his face. ' 'Tis a gran' life in th' counthry,' says he, 'far,' he says, 'fr'm th' madding crowd,' says he. 'Ye have no idee,' he says, 'how good it makes a man feel,' he says, 'to escape th' dust an' grime iv th' city,' he says, 'an' watch th' squrls at play,' he says. 'Whin I walk in me own garden,' he says, 'an' see th' viggytables comin' up, I hope, an' hear me own cow lowin' at th' gate iv th' fence,' he says, 'I f'rget,' he says, 'that they'se such a thing as a jint to be wiped or a sink to be repaired,' he says. He had a box iv viggytables an' a can iv condensed milk undher his arm. 'Th' wife is goin' away nex' week,' he says,

47

'do ye come out an' spind a few days with me,' he says. 'Not while I have th' strength to stay here,' says I. 'Well,' he says, 'maybe,' he says, 'I'll r-run in an' see ye,' he says. 'Is there annything goin' on at th' theayters?' he says.

"I wanst spint a night in th' counthry, Hinnissy. 'Twas whin Hogan had his villa out near th' river. 'Twas called a villa to distinguish it fr'm a house. If 'twas a little bigger 'twud be big enough f'r th' hens, an' if 'twas a little smaller 'twud be small enough f'r a dog. It looked as if 'twas made with a scroll saw, but Hogan mannyfacthered it himself out iv a design in th' pa-aper. 'How to make a country home on wan thousan' dollars. Puzzle: find th' money.' Hogan kidnapped me wan afthernoon an' took me out there in time to go to bed. He boosted me up a laddher into a bedroom adjinin' th' roof. 'I hope,' says I, 'I'm not discommodin' th' pigeons,' I says. 'There ain't anny pigeons here,' says he. 'What's that?' says I. 'That's a mosquito,' says he. 'I thought ye didn't have anny here,' says I. ''Tis th' first wan I've seen,' says he, whackin' himsilf on th' back iv th' neck. 'I got ye that time, assassin,' he says, hurlin' th' remains to the ground. 'They on'y come,' he says, 'afther a heavy rain or a heavy dhry spell,' he says, 'or whin they'se a little rain,' he says, 'followed by some dhryness,' he says. 'Ye mustn't mind thim,' he says. 'A mosquito on'y lives f'r a day,' he says. ''Tis a short life an' a merry wan,' says I. 'Do they die iv indigisthion?' I says. So he fell down through th' thrap-dure an' left me alone.

"Well, I said me prayers an' got into bed an' lay there, thinkin' iv me past life an' wondherin' if th' house was on fire. 'Twas warrum, Hinnissy. I'll not deny it. Th' roof was near enough to me that I cud smell th' shingles, an' th' sun had been rollin' on it all day long, an' though it had gone away, it'd left a ray or two to keep th' place. But I'm a survivor iv th' gr-reat fire, an' I often go down to th' rollin'-mills, an' besides, mind ye, I'm iv that turn iv mind that whin it's hot I say 'tis hot an' lave it go at that. So I whispers to mesilf, 'I'll dhrop off,' I says, 'into a peaceful slumber,' I says, 'like th' healthy plowboy that I am,' says I. An' I counted as far as I knew how an' conducted a flock ov sheep in a steeplechase, an' I'd just begun f'r to wondher how th' las' thing I thought iv came into me head, whin a dog started to howl in th' yard. They was a frind iv this dog in th' nex' house that answered him an' they had a long chat. Some other dogs butted in to be companionable. I heerd Hogan rollin' in bed, an' thin I heerd him goin' out to get a dhrink iv wather. He thripped over a chair befure he lighted a match to look at th' clock. It seemed like an hour befure he got back to bed. Be this time th' dogs was tired an' I was thinkin' I'd take a nap, whin a bunch iv crickets undher me windows begun f'r to discoorse. I've heerd iv th' crickets on th' hearth, Hinnissy, an I used to think they were all th' money, but anny time they get on me hearth I buy me a pound iv insect powdher. I'd rather have a pianola on th' hearth anny day, an' Gawd save me fr'm that! An' so 'twas dogs an' mosquitoes an' crickets an' mosquitoes an' a screech-owl an' mosquitoes an' a whip-poor-will an' mosquitoes an' cocks beginnin' to crow at two in th' mornin' an' mosquitoes, so that whin th' sun bounced up an' punched me in th' eye at four I knew what th' thruth is, that th' counthry is th' noisiest place in th' wurruld. Mind ye, there's a roar in th' city, but in th' counthry th' noises beats on ye'er ear like carpet-tacks bein' driven into th' dhrum. Between th' chirp iv a cricket an' th' chirp iv th' hammer at th' mills, I'll take th' hammer. I can go to sleep in a boiler shop, but I spint th' rest iv that night at Hogan's settin' in th' bathtub.

"I saw him in th' mornin' at breakfast. We had canned peaches an' condinsed milk. 'Ye have ye'er valise,' says he. 'Aren't ye goin' to stay out?' 'I am not,' says I. 'Whin th' first rattler goes by ye'll see me on th' platform fleein' th' peace an' quiet iv th' counthry, f'r th' turmoil an' heat,' I says, 'an' food iv a gr-reat city,' I says. 'Stay on th' farm,' says I. 'Commune,' I says, 'with nature,' I says. 'Enjoy,' I says, 'th' simple rustic life iv th' merry farmer-boy that goes whistlin' to his wurruk befure breakfast,' says I. 'But I must go back,' I says, 'to th' city,' I says, 'where there is nawthin' to eat but what ye want and nawthin' to dhrink but what ye can buy,' I says. 'Where th' dust is laid be th' sprinklin' cart, where th' ice-man comes reg'lar an' th' roof-garden is in bloom an' ye're waked not be th' sun but be th' milkman,' I says. 'I want to be near a doctor whin I'm sick an' near eatable food whin I'm hungry, an' where I can put me hand out early in the mornin' an' hook in a newspaper,' says I. 'Th' city,' says I, 'is th' on'y summer resort f'r a man that has iver lived in th' city,' I says. An' so I come in.

"'Tis this way, Hinnissy, th' counthry was all right whin we was young and hearty, befure we become enfeebled with luxuries, d'ye mind. 'Twas all right whin we cud shtand it. But we're not so shtrong as we was. We're diff'rent men, Hinnissy. Ye may say, as Hogan does, that we're ladin' an artificyal life, but, be Hivins, ye might as well tell me I ought to be paradin' up an' down a hillside in a suit iv skins, shootin' th' antylope an' th' moose, be gorry, an' livin' in a cave, as to make me believe I ought to get along without sthreet-cars an' ilicthric lights an' illyvators an' sody-water an' ice. 'We ought to live where all th' good things iv life comes fr'm,' says Hogan. 'No,' says I. 'Th' place to live is in where all th' good things iv life goes to.' Ivrything that's worth havin' goes to th' city; th' counthry takes what's left. Ivrything that's worth havin' goes to th city an' is iced. Th' cream comes in an' th' skim milk stays; th' sunburnt viggytables is consumed be th' hearty farmer-boy an' I go down to Callaghan's store an' ate the sunny half iv a peach. Th' farmer-boy sells what he has f'r money an' I get the money back whin he comes to town in th' winther to see the exposition. They give us th' products iv th' sile an' we give thim cottage organs an' knockout dhrops, an' they think they've broke even. Don't lave anny wan con-vince ye th' counthry's th' place to live, but don't spread th' news yet f'r a while. I'm goin' to advertise 'Dooleyville be-th'-River. Within six siconds iv sthreet-cars an' railway thrains, an' aisy reach iv th' theayters an' ambulances. Spind th' summer far fr'm th' busy haunts iv th' fly an' th' bug be th' side iv th' purlin' ice-wagon.' I'll do it, I tell ye. I'll organize excursions an' I'll have th' poor iv th' counthry in here settin' on th' cool steps an' passin' th' can fr'm hand to hand; I'll take thim to th' ball-game an' th' theayter; I'll lave thim sleep till breakfast-time an' I'll sind thim back to their overcrowded homes to dhream iv th' happy life in town. I will so."

"I'm glad to hear ye say that," said Mr. Hennessy. "I wanted to go out to th' counthry but I can't unless I sthrike."

"That's why I said it," replied Mr. Dooley.

—"Mr. Dooley's Opinions."

Avarice and Generosity

"I never blame a man f'r bein' avaricyous in his ol' age. Whin a fellow gits so he has nawthin' else to injye, whin ivrybody calls him 'sir' or 'mister,' an' young people dodge him an' he sleeps afther dinner, an' folks say he's an ol' fool if he wears a

buttonhole bokay, an' his teeth is only tinants at will an' not
permanent fixtures, 'tis no more thin nach'ral that he shud begin
to look around f'r a way iv keepin' a grip on human s'ciety. It
don't take him long to see that th' on'y thing that's vin'rable in
age is money, an' he pro-ceeds to acquire anything that happens to be in sight, takin' it where he can find it, not where he
wants it, which is th' way to accumylate a fortune. Money
won't prolong life, but a few millyons judicyously placed in good
banks an' occas'nally worn on the person will rayjooce age.
Poor ol' men are always older thin poor rich men. In th'
almshouse a man is decrepit an' mournful-lookin' at sixty, but
a millyonaire at sixty is jus' in th' prime iv life to a friendly eye,
an' there are no others.

"It's aisier to th' ol' to grow rich thin it is to th' young. At
makin' money a man iv sixty is miles ahead iv a la-ad iv twinty-
five. Pollytics and bankin' is th' on'y two games where age
has the best iv it. Youth has betther things to attind to, an'
more iv thim. I don't blame a man f'r bein' stingy anny more
thin I blame him f'r havin' a bad leg. Ye know th' doctors
say that if ye don't use wan iv ye'er limbs f'r a year or so ye can
niver use it again. So it is with gin'rosity. A man starts arly
in life not bein' gin'rous. He says to himsilf, 'I wurruked f'r
this thing an' if I give it away I lose it.' He ties up his gin'rosity
in bandages so that th' blood can't circlate in it. It gets to
be a superstition with him that he'll have bad luck if he iver
does annything f'r annybody. An' so he rakes in an' puts his
private mark with his teeth on all th' movable money in th'
wurruld. But th' day comes whin he sees people around him
gettin' a good dale iv injyemint out iv gin'rosity, an' somewan
says: 'Why don't ye, too, be gin-rous? Come, ol' green goods,
unbelt, loosen up, be gin-rous.' 'Gin'rous?' says he. 'What's
that?' 'It's th' best spoort in th' wurruld. It's givin' things

to people.' 'But I can't,' he says. 'I haven't annything to do it with,' he says. 'I don't know th' game. I haven't anny gin'rosity,' he says. 'But ye have,' says they. 'Ye have as much gin'rosity as anny wan if ye'll only use it,' says they. 'Take it out iv th' plasther cast ye put it in an' 'twill look as good as new,' says they. An' he does it. He thries to use his gin'rosity but all th' life is out iv it. It gives way undher him an' he falls down. He can't raise it fr'm th' ground. It's ossyfied an' useless. I've seen manny a fellow that suffered fr'm ossyfied gin'rosity.

"Whin a man begins makin' money in his youth at annything but games iv chance he niver can become gin'rous late in life. He may make a bluff at it. Some men are gin'rous with a crutch. Some men get the use of their gin'rosity back suddenly whin they ar-re in danger. Whin Clancy the miser was caught in a fire in th' Halsted Sthreet Palace Hotel he howled fr'm a window: 'I'll give twinty dollars to anny wan that'll take me down.' Cap'n Minehan put up a laddher an' climbed to him an' carrid him to th' sthreet. Half-way down th' laddher th' brave rayscooer was seen to be chokin' his helpless burdhen. We discovered aftherward that Clancy had thried to begin negotyations to rayjooce th' reward to five dollars. His gin'rosity had become suddenly par'lyzed again.

"So if ye'd stay gin'rous to th' end, niver lave ye'er gin'rosity idle too long. Don't run it ivry hour at th' top ov its speed, but fr'm day to day give it a little gintle exercise to keep it supple an' hearty an' in due time ye may injye it."

—"*Observations of Mr. Dooley.*"

Work and Sport

"A HARD time th' rich have injyin' life," said Mr. Dooley.

"I'd thrade with thim," said Mr. Hennessy.

"I wud not," said Mr. Dooley. "'Tis too much like hard wurruk. If I iver got hold iv a little mound iv th' money, divvle th' bit iv hardship wud I inflict on mesilf. I'd set on a large Turkish sofa an' have dancin' girls dancin' an' a mandolin or-chesthree playin' to me. I wudden't move a step without bein' carrid. I'd go to bed with th' lark an' get up with th' night-watchman. If anny wan suggested physical exercise to me, I'd give him forty dollars to go away. I'd hire a prize-fighter to do me fightin' f'r me, a pedesthreen to do me walkin', a jockey to do me ridin', an' a colledge pro-fissor to do me thinkin'. Here I'd set with a naygur fannin' me with osterich feathers, lookin' ca'mly out through me stained-glass windies on th' rollin'-mills, smokin' me good five-cint seegar an' rejicin' to know how bad ye mus' be feelin' ivry time ye think iv me hoorded wealth.

"But that ain't the way it comes out, Hinnissy. Higgins, th' millyionaire, had th' same idee as me whin he was beginnin' to breed money with a dollar he ownded an' a dollar he took fr'm some wan that wasn't there at th' time. While he was ham-merin' hoops on a bar'l or dhrivin' pegs into a shoe, he'd stop wanst in awhile to wipe th' sweat off his brow whin th' boss wasn't lookin' an' he'd say to himself: 'If I iver get it, I'll have a man wheel me around on a chair.' But as his stable grows an' he herds large dhroves down to th' bank ivry week, he changes his mind, an' whin he's got enough to injye life, as they say, he finds he's up against it. His throubles has just begun.

F. P. Dunne

I know in his heart Higgins's ideel iv luxury is enough buck-wheat cakes an' a cozy corner in a Turkish bath, but he can't injye it. He mus' be up an' doin'. An' th' on'y things anny wan around him is up an' doin' is th' things he used to get paid f'r doin' whin he was a young man.

"Arly in th' mornin' Higgins has got to be out exercisin' a horse to keep th' horse in good health. Higgins has no busi-ness on a horse an' he knows it. He was built an' idycated f'r a cooper, an' th' horse don't fit him. Th' nachral way f'r Hig-gins to ride a horse is to set well aft an' hang onto th' ears. But he's tol' that's wrong an' he's made to set up sthraight an' be a good fellow an' meet th' horse half way. An' if th' horse don't run away with Higgins an' kill him, he's tol' it's not a good horse an' he ought to sell it. An' mind ye, he pays f'r that though he can't help raymimberin' th' man nex' dure fr'm him used to get tin dollars a week f'r th' same job.

"When he was a young man, Higgins knowed a fellow that dhruv four horses f'r a brewery. They paid him well, but he hated his job. He used to come in at night an' wish his parents had made him a cooper, an' Higgins pitied him, knowin' he cudden't get out a life-insurance policy an' his wife was scared to death all th' time. Now that Higgins has got th' money, he's took th' brewery man's job with worse horses an' him barred f'm dhrivin' with more thin wan hand. An' does he get annything f'r it? On th' conth'ry, Hinnissy, it sets him back a large forchune. An' he says he's havin' a good time, an' if th' brewery man come along an' felt sorry f'r him Higgins wudden't exactly know why.

"Higgins has to sail a yacht raymimberin' how he despised th' Swede sailors that used to loaf in th' saloon near his house durin' th' winter; he has to run an autymobill, which is th' same thing as dhrivin' a throlley car on a windy day, without pay;

he has to play golf, which is th' same thing as bein' a letther-carryer without a dacint uniform; he has to play tennis, which is another wurrud f'r batin' a carpet; he has to race horses, which is the same thing as bein' a bookmaker with th' chances again' ye; he has to go abroad, which is th' same thing as bein' an immigrant; he has to set up late, which is th' same thing as bein' a dhrug clerk; an' he has to play cards with a man that knows how, which is th' same thing as bein' a sucker.

"He takes his good times hard, Hinnissy. A rich man at spoort is a kind iv non-union laborer. He don't get wages f'r it an' he don't dhrive as well as a milkman, ride as well as a stable-boy, shoot as well as a polisman, or autymobill as well as th' man that runs th' steam-roller. It's a tough life. They'se no rest f'r th' rich an' weary.

"We'll be readin' in th' pa-apers wan iv these days: 'Alonzo Higgins, th' runner up in las' year's champeenship, showed gr-reat improvement in this year's bricklayin' tournymint at Newport, an' won handily with about tin square feet to spare. He was nobly assisted by Regynald Van Stinyvant, who acted as his hod-carryer an' displayed all th' agility which won him so much applause arlier in th' year.'

"'Th' Pickaways carrid off all th' honors in th' sewer-diggin' contest yesterdah, defatin' th' Spadewells be five holes to wan. Th' shovel wurruk iv Cassidy th' banker was spicially notice-able. Th' colors iv th' Pickaways was red flannel undher-shirts an' dark-brown trousers.'

"'Raycreations iv rich men: Jawn W. Grates an' J. Pierpont Morgan ar-re to have a five-days' shinglin' contest at Narragan-sett Pier. George Gold is thrainin' f'r th' autumn plumbin' jimkanny. Mitchigan Avnoo is tore up fr'm Van Buren Sthreet to th' belt line in priparation f'r th' contest in shreet-layin' between mimbers iv th' Assocyation iv More-Thin-Rich

Spoorts. Th' sledge teams is completed, but a few good tampers an' wather men is needed.'

"An' why not, Hinnissy? If 'tis fun to wurruk, why not do some rale wurruk? If 'tis spoort to run an autymobill, why not run a locymotive? If dhrivin' a horse in a cart is a game, why not dhrive a delivery wagon an' carry things around? Sure, I s'pose th' raison a rich man can't undherstand why wages shud go higher is because th' rich can't see why annybody shud be paid f'r annything so amusin' as wurruk. I bet ye Higgins is wondherin' at this moment why he was paid so much f'r puttin' rings around a bar'l.

"No, sir, what's a rich man's raycreation is a poor man's wurruk. Th' poor ar-re th' on'y people that know how to injye wealth. Me idee iv settin' things sthraight is to have th' rich who wurruk because they like it do th' wurruk f'r th' poor who wud rather rest. I'll be happy th' day I see wan iv th' Hankerbilts pushin' ye'er little go-cart up th' platform while ye set in th' shade iv a three an' cheer him on his way. I'm sure he'd do it if ye called it a spoort an' tol him th' first man t' th' dump wud be entitled to do it over again against sthronger men nex' week. Wud ye give him a tin cup that he cud put his name on? Wud ye, Hinnissy? I'm sure ye wud."

"Why do they do it?" asked Mr. Hennessy.

"I dinnaw," said Mr. Dooley, "onless it is that th' wan great object iv ivry man's life is to get tired enough to sleep. Ivrything seems to be some kind iv wurruk. Wurruk is wurruk if ye're paid to do it, an' it's pleasure if ye pay to be allowed to do it."—*Observations of Mr. Dooley.*

George Horace Lorimer

The Advantages of Travel

DEAR PIERREPONT: Your letter of the seventh twists around
the point a good deal like a setter pup chasing his tail. But I
gather from it that you want to spend a couple of months in
Europe before coming on here and getting your nose in the bull-
ring. Of course you are your own boss now and you ought to
be able to judge better than any one else how much time you
have to waste, but it seems to me, on general principles, that a
young man of twenty-two, who is physically and mentally sound,
and who hasn't got a dollar and has never earned one, can't
be getting on somebody's pay-roll too quick. And in this connection it is only fair to tell you that I have instructed the
cashier to discontinue your allowance after July 15th. That
gives you two weeks for a vacation—enough to make a sick
boy well, or a lazy one lazier.

I hear a good deal about men who won't take vacations, and
who kill themselves by overwork, but it's usually worry or
whisky. It's not what a man does during working-hours, but
after them, that breaks down his health. A fellow and his business should be bosom friends in the office and sworn enemies
out of it. A clear mind is one that is swept clean of business
at six o'clock every night and isn't open up for it again until
after the shutters are taken down next morning.

Some fellows leave the office at night and start out to whoop
it up with the boys, and some go home to sit up with their troubles—they're both in bad company. They're the men who are

always needing vacations, and never getting any good out of them. What every man does need once a year is a change of work—that is, if he has been curved up over a desk for fifty weeks and subsisting on birds and burgundy, he ought to take to fishing for a living and try bacon and eggs, with a little spring water, for dinner. But coming from Harvard to the packing-house will give you change enough this year to keep you in good trim, even if you didn't have a fortnight's leeway to run loose.

You will always find it a safe rule to take a thing just as quick as it is offered—especially a job. It is never easy to get one except when you don't want it; but when you have to get work, and go after it with a gun, you'll find it as shy as an old crow that every farmer in the county has had a shot at.

When I was a young fellow and out of a place, I always made it a rule to take the first job that offered, and to use it for bait. You can catch a minnow with a worm, and a bass will take your minnow. A good fat bass will tempt an otter, and then you've got something worth skinning. Of course there's no danger of your not being able to get a job with the house—in fact, there is no real way in which you can escape getting one; but I don't like to see you shy off every time the old man gets close to you with the halter.

I want you to learn right at the outset not to play with the spoon before you take the medicine. Putting off an easy thing makes it hard, and putting off a hard one makes it impossible. Procrastination is the longest word in the language, but there's only one letter between its ends when they occupy their proper places in the alphabet.

Old Dick Stover, for whom I once clerked in Indiana, was the worst hand at procrastinating that I ever saw. Dick was a powerful hearty eater, and no one ever loved meal-time better, but he used to keep turning over in bed mornings for just another wink and staving off getting up, until finally his wife combined breakfast and dinner on him, and he only got two meals a day. He was a mighty religious man, too, but he got to putting off saying his prayers until after he was in bed, and then he would keep passing them along until his mind was clear of worldly things, and in the end he would drop off to sleep without saying them at all. What between missing the Sunday morning service and never being seen on his knees, the first thing Dick knew he was turned out of the church. He had a pretty good business when I first went with him, but he would keep putting off firing his bad clerks until they had lit out with the petty cash; and he would keep putting off raising the salaries of his good ones until his competitor had hired them away. Finally, he got so that he wouldn't discount his bills, even when he had the money; and when they came due he would give notes so as to keep from paying out his cash a little longer. Running a business on those lines is, of course, equivalent to making a will in favor of the sheriff and committing suicide so that he can inherit. The last I heard of Dick he was ninety-three years old and just about to die. That was ten years ago, and I'll bet he's living yet. I simply mention Dick in passing as an instance of how habits rule a man's life.

There is one excuse for every mistake a man can make, but only one. When a fellow makes the same mistake twice he's got to throw up both hands and own up to carelessness or cussedness. Of course I knew that you would make a fool of yourself pretty often when I sent you to college, and I haven't been disappointed. But I expected you to narrow down the number of combinations possible by making a different sort of a fool of yourself every time. That is the important thing, unless a fellow has too lively an imagination, or has none at all. You are bound to try this European foolishness sooner or later, but if you will wait a few years, you will approach it in an entirely different spirit—and you will come back with a good deal of respect for the people who have sense enough to stay at home.

I piece out from your letter that you expect a few months on the other side will sort of put a polish on you. I don't want to seem pessimistic, but I have seen hundreds of boys graduate from college and go over with the same idea, and they didn't bring back a great deal except a few trunks of badly fitting clothes. Seeing the world is like charity—it covers a multitude of sins, and, like charity, it ought to begin at home.

Culture is not a matter of a change of climate. You'll hear more about Browning to the square foot in the Mississippi Valley than you will in England. And there's as much Art talk on the Lake front as in the Latin Quarter. It may be a little different, but it's there.

I went to Europe once myself. I was pretty raw when I left Chicago, and I was pretty sore when I got back. Coming and going I was simply sick. In London, for the first time in my life, I was taken for an easy thing. Every time I went into a store there was a bull movement. The clerks all knocked off their regular work and started in to mark up prices.

They used to tell me that they didn't have any gold-brick men over there. So they don't. They deal in pictures—old masters, they call them. I bought two—you know the ones—those hanging in the waiting-room at the stock-yards; and when I got back I found out that they had been painted by a measly little fellow who went to Paris to study art, after Bill Harris had found out that he was no good as a settling clerk. I keep 'em to remind myself that there's no fool like an old American fool when he gets this picture paresis.

The fellow who tried to fit me out with a coat-of-arms didn't find me so easy. I picked mine when I first went into business for myself—a charging steer—and it's registered at Washington. It's my trade-mark, of course, and that's the only coat-of-arms an American merchant has any business with. It's penetrated to every quarter of the globe in the last twenty years, and every soldier in the world has carried it—in his knapsack.

I take just as much pride in it as the fellow who inherits his and can't find any place to put it, except on his carriage-door and his letter-head—and it's a heap more profitable. It's got so now that every jobber in the trade knows that it stands for good quality, and that's all any Englishman's coat-of-arms can stand for. Of course an American's can't stand for anything much—generally it's the burned-in-the-skin brand of a snob.

After the way some of the descendants of the old New York Dutchmen with the hoe and the English general storekeepers have turned out, I sometimes feel a little uneasy about what my great-grandchildren may do, but we'll just stick to the trade-mark and try to live up to it while the old man's in the saddle.

I simply mention these things in a general way. I have no fears for you after you've been at work for a few years, and have struck an average between the packing-house and Harvard; then, if you want to graze over a wider range, it can't hurt you. But for the present you will find yourself pretty busy trying to get into the winning class.

Your affectionate father,

JOHN GRAHAM.

—"*Letters from a Self-Made Merchant to His Son.*"

George Horace Lorimer

Good Counsel

JULY 7, 189-.

DEAR PIERREPONT: Yours of the fourth has the right ring, and it says more to the number of words used than any letter that I have ever received from you. I remember reading once that some fellows use language to conceal thought; but it's been my experience that a good many more use it *instead* of thought.

A business man's conversation should be regulated by fewer and simpler rules than any other function of the human animal. They are:

Have something to say.

Say it.

Stop talking.

Beginning before you know what you want to say and keeping on after you have said it lands a merchant in a lawsuit or the poorhouse, and the first is a short cut to the second. I maintain a legal department here, and it costs a lot of money, but it's to keep me from going to law.

It's all right when you are calling on a girl or talking with friends after dinner to run a conversation like a Sunday-school excursion, with stops to pick flowers; but in the office your sentences should be the shortest distance possible between periods. Cut out the introduction and the peroration, and stop before you get to secondly. You've got to preach short sermons to catch sinners; and deacons won't believe they need long ones themselves. Give fools the first and women the last word. The meat's always in the middle of the sandwich. Of course a little butter on either side of it doesn't do any harm if it's intended for a man who likes butter.

Remember, too, that it's easier to look wise than to talk wisdom. Say less than the other fellow and listen more than you talk; for when a man's listening he isn't telling on himself and he's flattering the fellow who is. Give most men a good listener and most women enough note-paper and they'll tell all they know. Money talks—but not unless its owner has a loose tongue, and then its remarks are always offensive. Poverty talks, too, but nobody wants to hear what it has to say.

I simply mention these things in passing because I'm afraid you're apt to be the fellow who's doing the talking; just as I'm a little afraid that you're sometimes like the hungry drummer at the dollar-a-day house—inclined to kill your appetite by eating the cake in the center of the table before the soup comes on.

Of course I'm glad to see you swing into line and show the proper spirit about coming on here and going to work; but you mustn't get yourself all "het up" before you take the plunge, because you're bound to find the water pretty cold at first. I've seen a good many young fellows pass through and out of this office. The first week a lot of them go to work they're in a sweat for fear they'll be fired; and the second week for fear they won't be. By the third, a boy that's no good has learned just how little work he can do and keep his job; while the fellow who's got the right stuff in him is holding down his own place with one hand and beginning to reach for the job just ahead of him with the other. I don't mean that he's neglecting his work; but he's beginning to take notice, and that's a mighty hopeful sign in either a young clerk or a young widow.

You've got to handle the first year of your business life about the way you would a trotting horse. Warm up a little before going to the post—not enough to be in a sweat, but just enough to be limber and eager. Never start off at a gait that you can't improve on, but move along strong and well in hand to the quarter. Let out a notch there, but take it calm enough up to the half not to break, and hard enough not to fall back into the ruck. At the three-quarters you ought to be going fast enough to poke your nose out of the other fellow's dust, and running like the Limited in the stretch. Keep your eyes to the front all the time, and you won't be so apt to shy at the little things by the side of the track. Head up, tail over the dashboard—that's the way the winners look in the old pictures of Maud S. and Dexter and Jay-Eye-See. And that's the way I want to see you swing by the old man at the end of the year, when we hoist the numbers of the fellows who are good enough to promote and pick out the salaries which need a little sweetening.

I've always taken a good deal of stock in what you call "Blood-will-tell" if you're a Methodist, or "Heredity" if you're a Unitarian; and I don't want you to come along at this late day and disturb my religious beliefs. A man's love for his children and his pride are pretty badly snarled up in this world, and he can't always pick them apart. I think a heap of you and a heap of the house, and I want to see you get along well together. To do that you must start right. It's just as necessary to make a good first impression in business as in courting. You'll read a good deal about "love at first sight" in novels, and there may be something in it for all I know; but I'm dead certain there's no such thing as love at first sight in business. A man's got to keep company a long time, and come early and stay late and sit close, before he can get a girl or a job worth having. There's nothing comes without calling in this world, and after you've called you've generally got to go and fetch it yourself.

Our bright young men have discovered how to make a pretty good article of potted chicken, and they don't need any help from hens, either; and you can smell the clover in our butterine if you've developed the poetic side of your nose; but none of the boys have been able to discover anything that will pass as a substitute for work, even in a boarding-house, though I'll give some of them credit for having tried pretty hard.

I remember when I was selling goods for old Josh Jennings, back in the sixties, and had rounded up about a thousand in a savings-bank—a mighty hard thousand, that came a dollar or so at a time, and every dollar with a little bright mark where I had bit it—I roomed with a dry-goods clerk named Charlie Chase. Charlie had a hankering to be a rich man; but somehow he could never see any connection between that hankering and his counter, except that he'd hint to me sometimes about an heiress who used to squander her father's money shamefully for the sake of having Charlie wait on her. But when it came to getting rich outside the dry-goods business and getting rich in a hurry, Charlie was the man.

Along about Tuesday night—he was paid on Saturday—he'd stay at home and begin to scheme. He'd commence at eight o'clock and start a magazine, maybe, and before midnight he'd be turning away subscribers because his presses couldn't print a big enough edition. Or perhaps he wouldn't feel literary that night, and so he'd invent a system for speculating in wheat and go on pyramiding his purchases till he'd made the best that Cheops did look like a five-cent plate of ice-cream. All he ever needed was a few hundred for a starter, and to get that he'd decide to let me in on the ground floor. I want to say right here that whenever any one offers to let you in on the ground floor, it's a pretty safe rule to take the elevator to the roof-garden. I never exactly refused to lend Charlie the capital he needed, but we generally compromised on half a dollar next morning, when he was in a hurry to make the store to keep from getting docked.

He dropped by the office last week, a little bent and seedy, but all in a glow and trembling with excitement in the old way. Told me he was President of the Klondike Exploring, Gold Prospecting and Immigration Company, with a capital of ten millions. I guessed that he was the board of directors and the capital stock and the exploring and the prospecting and the immigrating too—everything, in fact, except the business card he'd sent in; for Charlie always had a gift for nosing out printers who'd trust him. Said that for the sake of old times he'd let me have a few thousand shares at fifty cents, though they would go to par in a year. In the end we compromised on a loan of ten dollars, and Charlie went away happy.

The swamps are full of razor-backs like Charlie, fellows who'd rather make a million a night in their heads than five dollars a day in cash. I have always found it cheaper to lend a man of that build a little money than to hire him. As a matter of fact, I have never known a fellow who was smart enough to think for the house days and for himself nights. A man who tries that is usually a pretty poor thinker, and he isn't much good to either; but if there's any choice the house gets the worst of it.

I simply mention these little things in a general way. If you can take my word for some of them you are going to save yourself a whole lot of trouble. There are others which I don't speak of because life is too short and because it seems to afford a fellow a heap of satisfaction to pull the trigger for himself to see if it is loaded; and a lesson learned at the muzzle has the virtue of never being forgotten.

You report to Milligan at the yards at eight sharp on the fifteenth. You'd better figure on being here on the fourteenth, because Milligan's a pretty touchy Irishman, and I may be able to give you a point or two that will help you to keep on his mellow side. He's apt to feel a little sore at taking on in his department a man whom he hasn't passed on.

Your affectionate father,

JOHN GRAHAM.

—*"Letters from a Self-Made Merchant to His Son."*

A Word to the Wise

CHICAGO, April 15, 189–.

DEAR PIERREPONT: Don't ever write me another of those sad, sweet, gentle sufferer letters. It's only natural that a colt should kick a trifle when he's first hitched up to the break wagon, and I'm always a little suspicious of a critter that stands too quiet under the whip. I know it's not meekness, but meanness, that I've got to fight, and it's hard to tell which is the worst.

The only animal which the Bible calls patient is an ass, and that's both good doctrine and good natural history. For I had to make considerable of a study of the Missouri mule when I was a boy, and I discovered that he's not really patient, but that he only pretends to be. You can cuss him out till you've nothing but holy thoughts left in you to draw on, and you can lay the rawhide on him till he's striped like a circus zebra, and if you're cautious and reserved in his company he will just look grieved and pained and resigned. But all the time that mule will be getting meaner and meaner inside, adding compound cussedness every thirty days, and practising drop kicks in his stall after dark.

Of course nothing in this world is wholly bad, not even a

68

mule, for he is half horse. But my observation has taught me that the horse half of him is the front half, and that the only really safe way to drive him is hind-side first. I suppose that you could train one to travel that way, but it really doesn't seem worth while when good roadsters are so cheap.

That's the way I feel about these young fellows who lazy along trying to turn in at every gate where there seems to be a little shade, and sulking and balking whenever you say "git-ap" to them. They are the men who are always howling that Bill Smith was promoted because he had a pull, and that they are being held down because the manager is jealous of them. I've seen a good many pulls in my time, but I never saw one strong enough to lift a man any higher than he could raise himself by his boot-straps, or long enough to reach through the cashier's window for more money than its owner earned.

When a fellow brags that he has a pull, he's a liar or his employer's a fool. And when a fellow whines that he's being held down, the truth is, as a general thing, that his boss can't hold him up. He just picks a nice, soft spot, stretches out flat on his back, and yells that some heartless brute has knocked him down and is sitting on his chest.

A good man is as full of bounce as a cat with a small boy and a bull terrier after him. When he's thrown to the dog from the second-story window, he fixes while he's sailing through the air to land right, and when the dog jumps for the spot where he hits, he isn't there, but in the top of the tree across the street. He's a good deal like the little red-headed cuss that we saw in the football game you took me to. Every time the herd stampeded it would start in to trample and paw and gore him. One minute the whole bunch would be on top of him, and the next he would be loping off down the range, spitting out hair and pieces of canvas jacket, or standing on one side as cool as a hog on ice, watching the mess unsnarl and the removal of the cripples.

I didn't understand football, but I understood that little sawed-off. He knew his business. And when a fellow knows his business, he doesn't have to explain to people that he does. It isn't what a man knows, but what he thinks he knows, that he brags about. Big talk means little knowledge.

There's a vast difference between having a carload of miscellaneous facts sloshing around loose in your head and getting all mixed up in transit, and carrying the same assortment properly boxed and crated for convenient handling and immediate delivery. A ham never weighs so much as when it's half cured. When it has soaked in all the pickle that it can, it has to sweat out most of it in the smoke-house before it is any real good; and when you've soaked up all the information you can hold, you will have to forget half of it before you will be of any real use to the house. If there's anything worse than knowing too little, it's knowing too much. Education will broaden a narrow mind, but there's no known cure for a big head. The best you can hope is that it will swell up and bust; and then, of course, there's nothing left. Poverty never spoils a good man, but prosperity often does. It's easy to stand hard times, because that's the only thing you can do, but in good times the fool-killer has to do night-work.

I simply mention these things in a general way. A good many of them don't apply to you, no doubt, but it won't do any harm to make sure. Most men get cross-eyed when they come to size themselves up, and see an angel instead of what they're trying to look at. There's nothing that tells the truth to a woman like a mirror, or that lies harder to a man.

What I am sure of is that you have got the sulks too quick. If you knew all that you'll have to learn before you'll be a big, broad-gaged merchant, you might have something to be sulky about.

When you've posted yourself properly about the business you'll have taken a step in the right direction—you will be able to get your buyer's attention. All the other steps are those which lead you into his confidence.

Right here you will discover that you are in the fix of the young fellow who married his best girl and took her home to live with his mother. He found that the only way in which he could make one happy was by making the other mad, and that when he tried to make them both happy he only succeeded in making them both mad. Naturally, in the end, his wife divorced him and his mother disinherited him, and left her money to an orphan asylum, because, as she sensibly observed in the codicil, "orphans cannot be ungrateful to their parents." But if the man had had a little tact he would have kept them in separate houses, and have let each one think that she was getting a trifle the best of it, without really giving it to either.

Tact is the knack of keeping quiet at the right time; of being so agreeable yourself that no one can be disagreeable to you; of making inferiority feel like equality. A tactful man can pull the stinger from a bee without getting stung.

Some men deal in facts, and call Bill Jones a liar. They get knocked down. Some men deal in subterfuges, and say that Bill Jones's father was a kettle-rendered liar, and that his mother's maiden name was Sapphira, and that any one who believes in the Darwinian theory should pity rather than blame their son. They get disliked. But your tactful man says that since Baron Munchausen no one has been so chuck full of bully reminiscences as Bill Jones; and when that comes back to Bill he is half tickled to death, because he doesn't know that the higher criticism has hurt the Baron's reputation. That man gets the trade.

There are two kinds of information: one to which everybody's entitled, and that is taught at school; and one which nobody ought to know except yourself, and that is what you think of Bill Jones. Of course, where you feel a man is not square you will be armed to meet him, but never on his own ground. Make him be honest with you if you can, but don't let him make you dishonest with him.

When you make a mistake, don't make the second one, keeping it to yourself. Own up. The time to sort out rotten eggs is at the nest. The deeper you hide them in the case the longer they stay in circulation, and the worse impression they make when they finally come to the breakfast table. A mistake sprouts a lie when you cover it up. And one lie breeds enough distrust to choke out the prettiest crop of confidence that a fellow ever cultivated.

Of course it's easy to have the confidence of the house, or the confidence of the buyer, but you've got to have both. The house pays you your salary, and the buyer helps you earn it. If you skin the buyer you will lose your trade; and if you play tag with the house you will lose your job. You've simply got to walk the fence straight, for if you step to either side you'll find a good deal of air under you.

Even after you are able to command the attention and the confidence of your buyers, you've got to be up and dressed all day to hold what trade is yours, and twisting and turning all night to wriggle into some of the other fellow's. When business is good, that is the time to force it, because it will come easy; and when it is bad, that is the time to force it, too, because we will need the orders.

Speaking of making trade, naturally calls to my mind my old

acquaintance, Herr Doctor Paracelsus Von Munsterberg, who, when I was a boy, came to our town, "fresh from his healing triumphs at the Courts of Europe," as his handbills ran, "not to make money, but to confer on suffering mankind the priceless boon of health; to make the sick well, and the well better."

Munsterberg wasn't one of your common, coarse, county-fair barkers. He was a pretty high-toned article. Had nice, curly black hair, and didn't spare the bear's grease. Wore a silk hat and a Prince Albert coat all the time, except when he was orating, and then he shed the coat to get freer action with his arms. And when he talked he used the whole language, you bet.

Of course the priceless boon was put up in bottles, labeled Munsterberg's Miraculous Medical Discovery, and, simply to introduce it, he was willing to sell the small size at fifty cents and the large one at a dollar. In addition to being a philanthropist, the doctor was quite a hand at card tricks, played the banjo, sung coon songs, and imitated a saw going through a board very creditably. All these accomplishments, and the story of how he cured the Emperor of Austria's sister with a single bottle, drew a crowd, but they didn't sell a drop of the Discovery. Nobody in town was really sick, and those who thought they were had stocked up the week before with Quackenboss' Quick Quinine Kure from a fellow that made just as liberal promises as Munsterberg, and sold the large size at fifty cents, including a handsome reproduction of an old master for the parlor.

Some fellows would just have cussed a little and have moved on to the next town, but Munsterberg made a beautiful speech, praising the climate, and saying that in his humble capacity he had been privileged to meet the strength and beauty of many courts, but never had he been in any place where strength was stronger or beauty beautifuller than right here in Hoskins's Corners. He prayed with all his heart, though it was almost too much to hope, that the cholera, which was raging in Kentucky, would pass this Eden by; that the yellow fever, which was devastating Tennessee, would halt abashed before this stronghold of health, though he felt bound to add that it was a peculiarly malignant and persistent disease; that the smallpox, which was creeping southward from Canada, would smite the next town instead of ours, though he must own that it was no respecter of persons; that the diphtheria and scarlet fever, which were sweeping over New England and crowding the graveyards, could be kept from crossing the Hudson, though they were great travelers and it was well to be prepared for the worst; that we one and all might providentially escape chills, headaches, coated tongue, pains in the back, loss of sleep and that tired feeling, but it was almost too much to ask, even of such a generous climate. In any event, he begged us to beware of worthless nostrums and base imitations. It made him sad to think that to-day we were here, and that to-morrow we were running up an undertaker's bill, all for the lack of a small bottle of Medicine's greatest gift to Man.

I could see that this speech made a lot of women in the crowd powerful uneasy, and I heard the Widow Judkins say that she was afraid it was going to be "a mighty sickly winter," and she didn't know as it would do any harm to have some of that stuff in the house. But the doctor didn't offer the priceless boon for sale again. He went right from his speech into an imitation of a dog with a tin can tied to his tail, running down Main Street and crawling under Si Hooper's store at the far end of it —an imitation, he told us, to which the Sultan was powerful partial, "him being a cruel man and delighting in torturing the poor dumb beasts which the Lord has given us to love, honor, and cherish."

He kept this sort of thing up till he judged it was our bed-time, and then he thanked us "one and all for our kind atten-tion," and said that as his mission in life was to amuse as well as to heal, he would stay over till the next afternoon and give a special matinée for the little ones, whom he loved for the sake of his own golden-haired Willie, back there over the Rhine.

Naturally, all the women and children turned out the next afternoon, though the men had to be at work in the fields and the stores, and the doctor just made us roar for half an hour. Then, while he was singing an uncommon funny song, Mrs. Brown's Johnny let out a howl.

The doctor stopped short. "Bring the poor little sufferer here, madam, and let me see if I can soothe his agony," says he.

Mrs. Brown was a good deal embarrassed and more scared, but she pushed Johnny, yelling all the time, up to the doctor, who began tapping him on the back and looking down his throat. Naturally, this made Johnny cry all the harder, and his mother was beginning to explain that she "reckoned she must have stepped on his sore toe," when the doctor struck his forehead, cried "Eureka!" whipped out a bottle of the priceless boon, and forced a spoonful of it into Johnny's mouth. Then he gave the boy three slaps on the back and three taps on the stomach, ran one hand along his windpipe, and took a small button-hook out of his mouth with the other.

Johnny made all his previous attempts at yelling sound like an imitation when he saw this, and he broke away and ran toward home. Then the doctor stuck one hand in over the top of his vest, waved the button-hook in the other, and cried: "Woman, your child is cured! Your button-hook is found!"

Then he went on to explain that when baby swallowed safety-pins, or pennies, or fish-bones, or button-hooks, or any little household articles, that all you had to do was to give it a spoonful of the priceless boon, tap it gently fore and aft, hold your hand under its mouth, and the little article would drop out like chocolate from a slot-machine.

Every one was talking at once now, and nobody had any time for Mrs. Brown, who was trying to say something. Finally she got mad and followed Johnny home. Half an hour later the doctor drove out of the Corners, leaving his stock of the priceless boon distributed—for the usual consideration—among all the mothers in town.

It was not until the next day that Mrs. Brown got a chance to explain that while the boon might be all that the doctor claimed for it, no one in her house had ever owned a button-hook, because her old man wore jack-boots, and she wore congress shoes, and little Johnny wore just plain feet.

I simply mention the doctor in passing, not as an example in morals, but in methods. Some salesmen think that selling is like eating—to satisfy an existing appetite; but a good salesman is like a good cook—he can create an appetite when the buyer isn't hungry.

I don't care how good old methods are, new ones are better, even if they're only just as good. That's not so Irish as it sounds. Doing the same thing in the same way year after year is like eating a quail a day for thirty days. Along toward the middle of the month a fellow begins to long for a broiled crow or a slice of cold dog.

Your affectionate father,

JOHN GRAHAM.

—"*Letters of a Self-Made Merchant to His Son.*"

George V. Hobart

John Henry at the Musicale

DID you ever get ready and go to a musicale?

Isn't it the velvet goods?

They pulled off one at Jack Frothingham's last Wednesday evening, and I had to walk up and down the aisle with the rest of the bunch.

Mind you, I like Jack, so this is no secret conclave of the Anvil Association.

Only, I wish to put him wise, that when he gives his next musicale my address is Forest Avenue, in the woods.

When I reached Jack's house the Burnish Brothers were grabbing groutchy music out of a guitar that didn't want to give up, and the mad revel was on.

The Burnish Brothers part their hair in the middle, and always do "The Washington Post" march on their mandolins for an encore.

If Mr. Sousa ever catches them there'll be a couple of shine chord-squeezers away to the bad.

When the Burnish Brothers took a bow and backed off, we were all invited to listen to a soprano solo by Miss Imogene Lukewarm.

Somebody went around and locked the doors, so I made up my mind to die game.

A foolish friend once told Imogene she could sing, so she went out and bought up a bunch of tra-la-la's and began to beat them around the parlor.

When Imogene sings she makes faces at herself.

If she needs a high note she goes after it like she was calling the dachshund in to dinner.

Imogene sang "Sleep, Sweetly Sleep," and then kept us awake with her voice.

After Imogene crept back to her cave we had the first treat of the evening, and the shock was so sudden it jarred us.

Uncle Mil came out and quivered a violin obligato entitled "The Lost Sheep in the Mountain," and it was all there is.

Uncle Mil was the only green spot in the desert.

When he gathered the gourd up under his chin and allowed the bow to tiptoe over the bridge, you could hear the nightingale calling to its mate.

I wanted to get up a petition asking Uncle Mil to play all the evening and make us all happy, but Will Bruce wouldn't let me.

Will said he wasn't feeling very well, and he wanted to hear the rest of the program and feel worse.

He got his wish.

The next thing we had was Sibyl, the illusionist.

Sibyl did a lot of moldy tricks with cards, and every few minutes she fell down and sprained her sleight of hand.

Sibyl was a polish for sure.

Then Swift McGee, the boy monologist, flung himself in the breach and told a bunch of Bixbys.

It was a cruel occasion.

Swift had an idea that when it came to cracking merry boo-boos he could pull Lew Dockstader off the horse and leave him under the fence.

As a monologist Swift thought he had George Fuller Golden half-way across the bay, and Fred Niblo was screaming for help.

George V. Hobart

Swift often told himself that he could give Marshall P. Wilder six sure-fires and beat him down to the wire.

Swift is one of those low-foreheads who "write their own stuff" and say "I done it!"

After Swift had talked the audience into a chill, he pushed on and left us with a stone-bruise on our memories.

Then we had Rufus Nelson, the parlor prestidigitator.

He cooked an omelet in a silk hat, and when he gave the hat back to Ed Walker the poached eggs fell out and cuddled up in Ed's hair.

Rufus apologized, and said he'd do the trick over again if some one else would lend him a hat, but there was nothing doing.

When the contralto crawled under the ropes and began to tell us that the bells in the village rang ding-ding-dong, I was busy watching a goo-goo bird.

Did you ever spot one of those Glance-Givers?

This chap's name was Llewellyn Joyce, and he considered himself a perfect hellyon.

He thought all he had to do was to roll his lamps at a lassie and she was off the slate.

Llewellyn loved to sit around at the musicale and burn the belle of the ball with his goo-goo eyes.

Llewellyn needed a swift slap—that's what he needed.

Next we had the Nonpareil Quartet, and they were the boys that could eat up the close harmony!

They sang "Love, I am Lonely!" from start to finish without stopping to call the waiter.

Then we had Clarissa Coldslaw in select recitations.

She was all the money.

Clarissa grabbed "Hamlet's Soliloquy" between her pearly teeth and shook it to death.

She got a half-Nelson on Poe's "Raven" and put it out of the business.

Then she gave an imitation of the balcony scene from "Romeo and Juliet."

If Juliet talked like that dame did, no wonder she took poison.

But when she let down her hair and started to give us a mad scene—me to the sand dunes!

It was a case of flee as a bird with yours respectfully.

Those musicale things would be aces if the music didn't set them back.

John Henry at the Races

I was anxious to make Clara Jane think that she was all the money, so I boiled out a few plunks, trotted over to the trolley, and rushed her to the race-track.

I'm a dub on the dope, but it was my play to be a Wise Boy among the skates on this particular occasion, and I went the whole distance.

In the presence of my lady-love I knew every horse that ever pulled a harrow.

Isn't it cruel how a slob will cut the guy-ropes and go up in the air just because his Baby is by his side?

Me—to the mountain-tops!

Before the car got started I was telling her how Pittsburg Phil and I won $18,000 last summer on a fried fish they called Benzine.

Then I confided to her the fact that I doped a turtle named Pink Toes to win the next day, but he went over the fence after a loose bunch of grass and I lost $23,680.

George V. Hobart

She wanted to know what I meant by dope, and I told her it generally meant a sour dream, but she didn't seem to grab.

When we got to the track they were bunching the bones for the first race; so I told Clara Jane I thought I'd crawl down to the ring and plaster two or three thousand around among the needy. Two or three thousand, and me with nothing but a five-spot in my jeans, and the return ticket-money in that!

"Are you really going to bet?" she asked.

"Sure!" I said; "I've got a pipe!"

"Well, I hope you won't smoke it near me. I hate pipes!" she said.

"All right; I'll take my pipe down to the betting-ring and smoke it there!" I said, and we parted good friends.

In front of the grand stand I met Nash Martinetti.

He was holding a bunch of poppies, and he picked out one in the first race and handed it to me.

"A skinch!" said Nash. "Go as far as you like."

Then Ned Rose went into a cataleptic state and handed me the winner—by a block. It couldn't go wrong unless its feet fell out.

"Here you are, John Henry, the real Pietro!" said Ban Roberts; "play Pump-Handle straight and place! It's the road to wealth—believe me! All the others are behind the hill!"

Every Breezy Boy I met had a different hunch, and they called me into the wharf and unloaded.

I figured it out that if I had bet $5 on each good thing they gave me I would have lost $400,000.

Then I ducked under, sopped up a stein of root beer, and climbed up again to the hurricane-deck.

"Did you bet?" inquired Clara Jane.

"Only $730," I said; "a mere bag o' shells."

81

I leave a call for 7.30 every morning, and I suppose that's the reason I was so swift with the figures.

"My! what a lot of money!" said the Fair One. "Do point out the horse you bet on! I shall be awfully interested in this race!"

Carlo! you're a bad dog—lie down!

I pointed out the favorite as the one I had my bundle on, and explained to Clara Jane that the only way it could lose was for some sorehead to get out and turn the track around.

Sure enough, the favorite galloped into port and dropped anchor six hours ahead of the other clams.

I win over $2,200—conversation money—and Bonnie Bright-eyes was in a frenzy of delight.

She wanted to know if I wasn't going to be awfully careful with it and save it up for a rainy day.

I told her yes, but I expected we'd have a storm that afternoon.

I had a nervous chill for fear she'd declare herself in on the rake-off.

But she didn't, so I excused myself, and backed down the ladder to cash in.

The boys were all out in the inquest room, trying to find out what killed the dead ones.

Then they stopped apologizing to themselves, and began to pick things out of the next race and push them up their sleeves.

I ran across Harry Maddy, and he took me up to the roof with a line of talk about a horse called Pretty Boy in the last race.

"He'll be over 80 to 1, and it's a killing," Harry insisted. "Get down to the bank when the doors open and grab all you can. Take a satchel and the ice-tongs and haul it away."

I was beginning to be impressed.

George V. Hobart

"Put a fiver on Pretty Boy," Harry continued, "and you'll find yourself dropping over in the Pierp Morgan class before sundown."

"This may be a real Alexander," I said to myself.

"Pretty Boy can stop in the stretch to do a song and dance and still win by a bunch of houses," Harry informed me.

I began to think hard.

"Don't miss it," said Harry. "It's a moral that if you play him you'll die rich and disgraced, like our friend Andy, the Hoot, Mon!"

When I got back to the stand I had a preoccupied air.

The five-spot in my jeans was crawling around and begging for a change of scene.

When Clara Jane asked me how much I had bet on the race just about to start, I could only think of $900.

When she wanted to know which horse, I pointed my finger at every toad on the track, and said, "That one over there."

It won.

At the end of the third race I was $19,218 to the good.

Clara Jane had it down in black and white on the back of an envelope in figures that couldn't lie.

She said she was very proud of me, and that's where my finish bowed politely and stood waiting.

She told me that it was really very wrong to bet any more after such a run of luck, and made me promise that I wouldn't wring another dollar from the trembling hands of the poor book-makers.

I promised, but she didn't notice that I had my fingers crossed.

I simply had to have a roll to flash on the way home, so I took my lonely V and went out into the Promised Land after the nuggets Maddy had put me wise to.

"It will be just like getting money from Uncle Peter," I figured.

"A small steak from Pretty Boy," I said to Wise Samuel, the book-maker. "What's doing?"

Wise Samuel gave me the gay look-over.

"Take the ferry for Sioux Falls!" he said.

"Nix on the smart talk, Sammy!" I said. "Me for the Pretty Boy! How much?"

"A bundle for a bite—you're on a cold plate!" whispered Wise Samuel, but he couldn't throw me.

"I don't see any derricks to hoist the price with," I tapped him.

"Write your own ticket, then you to the woods!" said Sammy.

In a minute my fiver was up, and I was on the card to win $500 when my cute one came romping home.

I went back to Clara Jane, satisfied that in a few minutes I'd have a roll big enough to choke the tunnel.

"Not having any money on this race, you can watch it without the least excitement, can't you?" she said.

I said yes, and all the while I was scrapping with a lump in my throat the size of my fist.

When the horses got away, with Pretty Boy in front, I started in to stand on my head, but changed my mind and swallowed half the program.

Pretty Boy at the quarter! Me for Rector's till they put the shutters up!

Pretty Boy at the half! Me down to Tiffany's in the morning dragging tiaras away in a dray!

Pretty Boy at the three-quarter pole! Me doing the free library gag all over the place!

But just as they came in the stretch Pretty Boy forgot something and went back after it.

George V. Hobart

The roach quit me cold at the very door of the safety deposit vaults.

I was under the water a long time.

Finally I heard Clara Jane saying, "Isn't it lucky you didn't bet on this race? I believe you would have picked that foolish-looking horse that stopped over there to bite the fence!"

"I'm done! Turn me over!" I murmured, and then I rushed down among the ramblers and made a swift touch for the price of a couple of rides home.

On the way back Clara Jane made me promise again that I'd be awfully, awfully careful of my $19,218.

I promised her I would.

Oliver Herford

Child's Natural History

GEESE

Ev-er-y child who has the use
Of his sen-ses knows a goose.
Sees them un-der-neath the tree
Gath-er round the goose-girl's knee,
While she reads them by the hour
From the works of Scho-pen-hau-er.
How pa-tient-ly the geese at-tend!
But do they re-al-ly com-pre-hend
What Scho-pen-hau-er's driv-ing at?
Oh, not at all; but what of that?
Nei-ther do I; nei-ther does she;
And, for that mat-ter, nor does he.

A SEAL

See, children, the Fur-bear-ing Seal;
Ob-serve his mis-di-rect-ed zeal;
He dines with most ab-ste-mi-ous care
On Fish, Ice Water, and Fresh Air,
A-void-ing con-di-ments or spice
For fear his fur should not be nice
And fine and soft and smooth and meet
For Broad-way or for Re-gent Street;
And yet, some-how, I of-ten feel
(Though for the kind Fur-bear-ing Seal

Oliver Herford

I har-bor a Re-spect Pro-found)
He runs Fur-bear-ance in the ground.

THE ANT

My child, ob-serve the use-ful Ant,
   How hard she works each day;
She works as hard as ad-a-mant
   (That's very hard, they say).
She has no time to gal-li-vant;
She has no time to play.
Let Fi-do chase his tail all day;
   Let Kit-ty play at tag;
She has no time to throw away,
   She has no tail to wag;
She scur-ries round from morn till night;
   She nev-er, nev-er sleeps;
She seiz-es ev-er-y-thing in sight,
She drags it home with all her might,
   And all she takes she keeps.

THE YAK

This is the Yak, so *neg-li-gée;*
His coif-fure's like a stack of hay;
He lives so far from Any-where,
I fear the Yak neg-lects his hair,
And thinks, since there is none to see,
What mat-ter how un-kempt he be.
How would he feel if he but knew
That in this Pic-ture-book I drew
His Phys-i-og-no-my un-shorn,
   For chil-dren to de-ride and scorn?

THE HEN

Alas! my Child, where is the Pen
That can do justice to the Hen?
Like Royalty, she goes her way,
Laying foundations every day;
Though not for Public Buildings, yet
For Custard, Cake, and Omelet.
Or if too Old for such a use,
They have their Fling at some Abuse,
As when to Censure Plays Unfit
Upon the Stage they make a Hit.
Or at elections Seal the Fate
Of an Obnoxious Candidate.
No wonder, Child, we prize the Hen,
Whose Egg is Mightier than the Pen.

THE COW

The Cow is too well known, I fear,
To need an introduction here.
If She should vanish from earth's face,
It would be hard to fill her place;
For with the Cow would disappear
So much that every one holds Dear.
Oh, think of all the Boots and Shoes,
Milk Punches, Gladstone Bags, and Stews,
And Things too numerous to count,
Of which, my Child, she is the Fount.
Let's hope, at least, the Fount may last
Until *our* Generation's past.

Oliver Herford

Metaphysics

WHY and Wherefore set out one day
  To hunt for a wild Negation;
They agreed to meet at a cool retreat
  On the Point of Interrogation.

But the night was dark and they missed their mark,
  And, driven well-nigh to distraction,
They lost their ways in a murky maze
  Of utter abstruse abstraction.

Then they took a boat, and were soon afloat
  On a sea of Speculation;
But the sea grew rough, and their boat, though tough,
  Was split into an Equation.

As they floundered about in the waves of doubt,
  Rose a fearful Hypothesis,
Who gibbered with glee as they sank in the sea,
  And the last they saw was this:

On a rock-bound reef of Unbelief
  There sat the wild Negation;
Then they sank once more and were washed ashore
  At the Point of Interrogation.

Gold

Some take their gold
  In minted mold,
And some in harps hereafter,
  But give me mine
  In tresses fine,
And keep the change in laughter!

S. W. Gillinan

Finnigin to Flannigan

SUPERINTINDINT wuz Flannigan;
Boss av the siction wuz Finnigin;
Whiniver the kyars got offen the thrack,
An' muddled up things t' th' divil an' back,
Finnigin writ it to Flannigan,
Afther the wrick wuz all on ag'in;
   That is, this Finnigin
   Repoorted to Flannigan.

Whin Finnigin furst writ to Flannigan,
He writed tin pages—did Finnigin,
An' he tould jist how the smash occurred;
Full minny a tajus, blunderin' wurrd
Did Finnigin write to Flannigan
Afther the cars had gone on ag'in.
   That wuz how Finnigin
   Repoorted to Flannigan.

Now Flannigan knowed more than Finnigin—
He'd more idjucation, had Flannigan;
An' it wore'm clane an' complately out
To tell what Finnigin writ about
In his writin' to Muster Flannigan-
So he writed back to Finnigin:
   "Don't do sich a sin ag'in;
   Make 'em brief, Finnigin!"

Whin Finnigin got this from Flannigan,
He blushed rosy rid, did Finnigin;
An' he said: "I'll gamble a whole month's pa-ay
That it will be minny an' minny a da-ay
Befoore Sup'rintindint—that's Flannigan—
Gits a whack at this very same sin ag'in.
  From Finnigin to Flannigan
  Repoorts won't be long ag'in."

.   .   .   .

Wan da-ay, on the siction av Finnigin,
On the road sup'rintinded by Flannigan,
A rail give way on a bit av a curve,
An' some kyars went off as they made the swerve.
"There's nobody hurted," sez Finnigin,
"But repoorts must be made to Flannigan."
  An' he winked at McGorrigan,
  As married a Finnigin.

He wuz shantyin' thin, wuz Finnigin,
As minny a railroader's been ag'in,
An' the shmoky ol' lamp wuz burnin' bright
In Finnigin's shanty all that night—
Bilin' down his repoort, was Finnigin!
An' he writed this here: "Muster Flannigan:
  Off ag'in, on ag'in,
  Gone ag'in.—Finnigin."

Copyright by Life Publishing Company.

Paul West

The Cumberbunce

I STROLLED beside the shining sea;
I was as lonely as could be;
No one to cheer me in my walk
But stones and sand, which cannot talk—
Sand and stones and bits of shell,
Which never have a thing to tell.

But as I sauntered by the tide,
I saw a something at my side,
A something green, and blue, and pink,
And brown, and purple, too, I think.
I would not say how large it was;
I would not venture that, because
It took me rather by surprise,
And I have not the best of eyes.

Should you compare it to a cat,
I'd say it was as large as that;
Or should you ask me if the thing
Was smaller than a sparrow's wing,
I should be apt to think you knew,
And simply answer, "Very true!"

Well, as I looked upon the thing,
It murmured, "Please, sir, can I sing?"
And then I knew its name at once—
It plainly was a Cumberbunce.

You are amazed that I could tell
The creature's name so quickly?   Well,
I knew 'twas not a paper doll,
A pencil or a parasol,
A tennis-racket or a cheese,
And, as it was not one of these,
And I am not a perfect dunce—
It had to be a Cumberbunce!

With pleading voice and tearful eye,
It seemed as though about to cry.
It looked so pitiful and sad,
It made me feel extremely bad.
My heart was softened to the thing
That asked me if it, please, could sing.
Its little hand I longed to shake,
But, oh, it had no hand to take!

I bent, and drew the creature near,
And whispered in its pale-blue ear,
"What! sing, my Cumberbunce? You can!
Sing on, sing loudly, little man!"
The Cumberbunce, without ado,
Gazed sadly on the ocean blue,
And, lifting up its little head,
In tones of awful longing, said:

"Oh, I would sing of mackerel skies,
    And why the sea is wet,
Of jelly-fish and conger-eels,
    And things that I forget.
And I would hum a plaintive tune
    Of why the waves are hot

Paul West

As water boiling on a stove,
  Excepting that they're not!

"And I would sing of hooks and eyes,
  And why the sea is slant,
And gaily tips the little ships,
  Excepting that I can't!
I never sang a single song,
  I never hummed a note;
There is in me no melody,
  No music in my throat.

"So that is why I do not sing
Of sharks, or whales, or anything!"

I looked in innocent surprise,
My wonder showing in my eyes.
"Then why, oh Cumberbunce," I cried,
"Did you come walking at my side
And ask me if you, please, might sing,
When you could not warble anything?"

"I did not ask permission, sir,
I really did not, I aver.
You, sir, misunderstood me quite;
I did not ask you if I *might*.
Had you correctly understood,
You'd know I asked you if I *could*.
So, as I cannot sing a song,
Your answer, it is plain, was wrong.
The fact I could not sing I knew,
But wanted your opinion, too."

A voice came softly o'er the lea.
"Farewell! my mate is calling me!"

I saw the creature disappear;
Its voice, in parting, smote my ear:
"I thought all people understood
The difference 'twixt 'might' and 'could'!"

Guy Wetmore Carryl

The Touching Tenderness of King Karl the First

For hunger and thirst King Karl the First
    Had a stoical, stern disdain;
The food that he ordered consistently bordered
    On what is described as plain.
Much trouble his cook ambitiously took
    To tickle his frugal taste,
But all of his savory science and slavery
    Ended in naught but waste.

Said the steward: "The thing to tempt the king
    And charm his indifferent eye
No doubt is a tasty, delectable pasty—
    Make him a blackbird pie!"
The cook at these words baked twenty-four birds,
    And set them before the king,
And the two dozen odious, bold, and melodious
    Singers began to sing!

The king in surprise said: "Dozens of pies
    In the course of our life we've tried,
But never before us was served up a chorus
    Like this that we hear inside!"
With a thunderous look he ordered the cook
    And the steward before him brought,
And with a beatified smile, "He is satisfied!"
    Both of these innocents thought.

"Of sinners the worst," said Karl the First,
   "Is the barbarous ruffian that
A song-bird would slaughter, unless for his daughter
   Or wife he is trimming a hat.
We'll punish you so for the future you'll know
   That from mercy you can't depart.
Observe that your lenient, kind, intervenient
   King has a tender heart!"

He saw that the cook in a neighboring brook
   Was drowned (as he quite deserved),
And he ordered the steward at once to be skewered.
   (The steward was much unnerved.)
"It's a curious thing," said the merciful king,
   "That monarchs so tender are,
So oft we're affected that we have suspected that
   We are too kind by far."

.   .   .   .

THE MORAL: The mercy of men and of kings
Are apt to be wholly dissimilar things.
In spite of "The Merchant of Venice," we're pained
To note that the quality's sometimes strained.

Caffiard

Deus ex Machina

THE studio was tucked away in the extreme upper north-east corner of 13 ter Rue Visconti, higher even than that cin-quième, dearly beloved of the impecunious, and of whoso, between stairs and street odors, chooses the lesser evil, and is more careful of lungs than legs. After the six long flights had been achieved, around a sharp corner and up a little winding stairway was the door which bore the name of Pierre Vauquelin. Inside, after stumbling along a narrow hall as black as Erebus, and floundering through a curtained doorway, one came abruptly into the studio, and in all probability fell headlong over a little rattan stool, or an easel, or a box of paints, and was picked up by the host, and dusted, and put to rights, and made much of, like a bumped child. Thus restored to equanimity, one was better able to appreciate what Pierre called la Boîte.

The Box was a room eight meters in width by ten in length, with a skylight above, and a great, square window in the north wall, which atter sloped inward from floor to ceiling, by reason of the mansard roof. Of what might be called furniture there was but little—a Norman cupboard of black wood, heavily carved, a long divan contrived from various packing-boxes and well-worn rugs, a large, square table, a half dozen chairs, three easels, and a repulsive little stove with an interminable pipe, which, with its many twists and turns, gave one the impression of a thick, black snake, that had a moment before been swaying about in the room, and had suddenly found a hole in the roof through which to thrust its head.

But of minor things the Box was full to overflowing. The Norman cupboard was crammed with an assortment of crockery, much of it sadly nicked and cracked; the divan was strewn with boxes of broken pastels, paint-brushes, and palettes coated with dried colors; the table littered with papers, sketches, and books; and every chair had its own particular trap for the unwary, in the form of thumb-tacks or a glass half full of cloudy water; and in the midst of this chaos, late on a certain mid-May afternoon, stood the painter himself, with his hands thrust deep into the pockets of his corduroy trousers, and his back turned upon the portrait upon which he had been at work. It was evident that something untoward was in the air, because Pierre, who always smoked, was not smoking, and Pierre, who never scowled, was scowling.

In the Quartier—that Quartier which alone, of them all, is spelt with a capital Q—there was, in ordinary, no gayer, more happy-go-lucky type than this same Pierre. He lived, as did a thousand of his kind, on eighty sous a day (there were those who lived on less, pardi!), and breakfasted, and dined, at that—yes, and paid himself an absinthe at the Deux Magots at six o'clock, and a package of green cigarettes, into the bargain. For the rest of the time he was understood to be working on a portrait in his studio, and, what is more surprising, often was. There was nothing remarkable about Pierre's portraits, except that occasionally he sold one, and for money—for *actual money*, the astonishing animal! But if any part of the modest proceeds of such a transaction remained, after the rent had been paid and a new canvas purchased, it was not the *caisse d'épargne* which saw it, be sure of that! For Pierre lived always for the next twenty-four hours, and let the rest of time and eternity look out for themselves.

Yet he took his work seriously. That was the trouble. Even admitting that, thus far, his orders had come only from the more prosperous tradesmen of the Quartier, did that mean, *par exemple*, that they would not come in time from the millionaires of the sixteenth arrondissement? By no means whatever, said Pierre. To be sure, he had never had the *Salon* in the palm of his hand, so to speak; but what of that? Jean-Paul himself would tell you that it was all favoritism! So Pierre toiled away at his portrait-painting, and made a little competency, but, if the truth were told, no appreciable progress from year's beginning to year's end.

For once, however, his luck had played him false. The fat restaurateur, whose wife's portrait he had finished that afternoon and carried at top speed, with the paint not yet dry, to the Rue du Bac, was out of town on business, and would not return until the following evening; and that, so far as Pierre was concerned, was quite as bad as if he were not expected until the following year. Pierre's total wealth amounted to one five-franc piece and three sous, and he had been relying upon the restaurateur's four louis to enable him to fulfil his promise to Mimi. For the next day was her *fête*, and they were to have breakfasted in the country, and taken a boat upon the Seine, and returned to dine under the trees. Not at Suresnes or St. Cloud, ah, *non!* Something better than that—the true country, *sapristi!* at Poissy, twenty-eight kilometers from Paris. All of which meant at least a louis, and no doubt more! And where, demanded Pierre of the great north window, where was a louis to be found?

For there was a tacit understanding among the comrades in the Quartier that there must be no borrowing and lending of money. It was a clause of their creed, which had been adopted in the early days of their companionship, for what was clearly the greatest general good, the chances being that no one of them would ever possess sufficient surplus capital either to accommodate another or to repay an accommodation. For a moment, to be sure, the thought had crossed Pierre's mind, but he had rejected it instantly as impracticable. Aside from the unwritten compact, there was no one of them all who could have been of service, had he so willed. Even Jacques Courbet, who possessed a disposition which would have impelled him to chop off his right hand with the utmost cheerfulness if thereby he could have gratified a friend, was worse than useless in this emergency. Had it been a matter of forty sous—but a louis! As well have asked him for the Vénus de Milo, and had done with it.

So it was that, with the premonition of Mimi's disappointed eyes cutting great gaps in his tender heart, Pierre had four times shrugged his shoulders and quoted to himself this favorite scrap of his remarkable philosophy—"Oh, lala! All this will arrange itself!" and four times had paused, in the act of lighting a cigarette, and plunged again into the depths of despondent reverie. As he was on the point of again repeating this entirely futile operation, a distant clock struck six, and Pierre, remembering that Mimi must even now be waiting for him at the west door of St. Germain-des-Prés, clapped on his cap, and sallied forth into the gathering twilight.

It was *apéritif* hour at the Café des Deux Magots, and the long, leather-covered benches against the windows, and the double row of little marble-topped tables in front, were rapidly filling, as Pierre and Mimi took their places and ordered two *Turins à l'eau*. A group of American Beaux Arts men at their right were chattering in their uncouth tongue, with occasional scraps of Quartier slang, by way of local color, and now and again hailing a newcomer with exclamations, apparently of satisfaction, which began with "Hello!" The boulevard St. Germain was alive with people, walking past with the admirable lack of haste which distinguishes the Parisian, or waiting, in patient, voluble groups, for a chance to enter the constantly arriving and departing trams and omnibuses; and an unending succession of open cabs filed slowly along the curb, their drivers scanning the *terrasse* of the café for a possible fare. The air was full of that mingled odor of wet wood pavements and horse-chestnut blossoms which is the outward, invisible sign of that most wonderful of inward and spiritual combinations, Paris and spring! And at the table directly behind Pierre and Mimi sat Caffiard.

There was nothing about Caffiard to suggest a *deus ex machina*, or anything else, for that matter, except a preposterously corpulent old gentleman with an amiable smile. But in nothing were appearances ever more deceitful than in Caffiard. For it was he, with his enormous double chin, and his general air of harmless fatuity, who edited the little colored sheet entitled *La Blague*, which sent half Paris into convulsions of merriment every Thursday morning, and he who knew every caricaturist in town, and was beloved of them all for the heartiness of his appreciation and the liberality of his payments. In the first regard he was but one of many Parisian editors; but in the second he stood without a peer. Caran d'Ache, Léandre, Willette, Forain, Hermann Paul, Abel Faivre—they rubbed their hands when they came out of Caffiard's private office; and if the day chanced to be Saturday, there was something in their hands worth rubbing. A fine example, Caffiard!

Mimi's black eyes sparkled like a squirrel's as she watched Pierre over the rim of her tumbler of vermouth. She was far from being blind, Mimi; and already, though they had been together but six minutes, she had noted that unusual little pucker between his eyebrows, that sad little droop at the corners of his merry mouth. She told herself that Pierre had been overworking himself, that Pierre was tired, that Pierre needed cheering up. So Mimi, who was never tired, not even after ten hours in Madame Fraichel's millinery establishment, secretly declared war upon the unusual little pucker and the sad little droop.

"*Voyons donc*, my Pierrot!" she said. "It is not a funeral to which we go to-morrow, at least! Thou must be gay, for we have much to talk of, thou knowest. One dines at La Boîte?"

"The dinner is there, such as it is," replied Pierre gloomily.

"What it is now, is not the question," said Mimi, with confidence, "but what I make of it—*pas?* And then there is tomorrow! Oh, lala, lalala! What a pleasure it will be, if only the good God gives us beautiful weather. *Dis, donc*, great thunder-cloud, dost thou know it, this Poissy?"

Pierre had begun a caricature on the back of the wine-card, glancing now and again at his model, an old man selling newspapers on the curb. He shook his head without replying.

"*Eh, b'en*, my little one, thou mayest believe me that it is of all places the most beautiful! One eats at the Esturgeon, on the Seine—but *on* the Seine, with the water quite near, like that chair. He names himself Jarry, the proprietor, and it is a good type—fat and handsome. I adore him! Art thou jealous, species of thinness of a hundred nails? *B'en*, afterward, one takes a boat, and goes softly, softly down the little arm of the Seine, and creeps under the willows, and perhaps fishes. But no, for it is the closed season. But one sings, eh? What does one sing? *Voyons!*"

She bent forward, and in a little voice like an elf's, very thin and sweet, hummed a snatch of a song they both knew:

> "*C'est votre ami Pierrot qui vient vous voir:*
> *Bonsoir, madame la lune!*

"And then," she went on, as Pierre continued his sketch in silence, "and then, one disembarks at Villennes and has a Turin under the arbors of Bodin. Another handsome type, Bodin! *Flut! What* a man!"

Mimi paused suddenly, and searched his cloudy face with her earnest, tender little eyes.

"Pierrot," she said softly, "what hast thou? Thou art not angry with thy gosseline?"

Pierre surveyed the outline of the newspaper vender thoughtfully, touched it, here and there, with his pencil-point, squinted, and then pushed the paper toward the girl.

"Not bad," he said, replacing his pencil in his pocket.

But Mimi had no eyes for the caricature, and merely flicked the wine-card to the ground.

"Pierrot," she repeated.

Vauquelin plunged his hands in his pockets and looked at her.

"Well, then," he announced almost brutally, "we do not go to-morrow."

"*Pierre!*"

It was going to be much worse than he had supposed, this little tragedy. *Bon Dieu*, how pretty she was, with her startled, hurt eyes, already filling with tears, and her parted lips, and her little white hand, that had flashed up to her cheek at his words! Oh, much worse than he had supposed! But she must be told; there was nothing but that. So Pierre put his elbows on the table, and his chin in his hands, and brought his face close to hers.

"*Voyons!*" he explained, "thou dost not believe me angry! *Mais non, mais non!* But listen. It is I who am the next to the last of idiots, since I have never a sou in pocket, never! And the imbecile restaurateur, whose wife I have been painting, will not return until to-morrow, and so I am not paid. *Voilà!*"

He placed his five-franc piece upon the table, and shrugged his shoulders.

"One full moon!" he said, and piled the three sous upon it. "And three soldiers. As I sit here, that is all, until to-morrow night. We cannot go!"

Brave little Mimi! Already she was winking back her tears, and smiling.

"But that—that is nothing!" she answered. "I do not care to go. No—but truly! Look! We shall spend the day in the studio, and breakfast on the balcony, and pretend the Rue Visconti is the Seine."

"I am an empty siphon!" said Pierre, yielding to desperation.

"*Non!*" said Mimi firmly.

"I am a pierced basket, a box of matches!"

"*Non! non!*" said Mimi, with tremendous earnestness. "Thou art Pierrot, and I love thee! Let us say no more. I shall go back and prepare the dinner, and thou shalt remain and drink a Pernod. It will give thee heart. But follow quickly. Give me the key."

She laid her wide-spread hand on his, palm upward, like a little pink starfish.

"We go together, and I adore thee!" said Pierre, and kissed her in the sight of all men, and was not ashamed.

Caffiard leaned forward, picked up the fallen wine-card, pretended to consult it, and ponderously arose. As Pierre was turning the key in the door of the little apartment, they heard a sound of heavy breathing, and the *deus ex machina* came lumbering up the winding stair.

"Monsieur is seeking some one?" asked the painter politely.

There was no breath left in Caffiard. He was only able, by way of reply, to point at the top button of Pierre's coat, and nód helplessly; then, as Mimi ran ahead to light the gas, he labored along the corridor, staggered through the curtained doorway, stumbled over a rattan stool, was rescued by Pierre, and finally established upon the divan, very red and gasping.

For a time there was silence, Pierre and Mimi busying themselves in putting the studio to rights, with an instinctive courtesy which took no notice of their visitor's snorts and wheezes; and Caffiard taking note of his surroundings with his round, blinking eyes. Opposite him, against the wall, reposed the portrait of the restaurateur's wife, as dry and pasty as a stale cream cheese upon the point of crumbling, and on an easel was another— that of Monsieur Pantin, the rich shirt-maker of the boulevard St. Germain—on which Pierre was at work. A veritable atrocity this, with a green background which trespassed upon Monsieur Pantin's hair, and a featureless face, gaunt and haggard, with yellow and purple undertones. There was nothing in either picture to refute one's natural suspicion that soap had been the medium employed. Caffiard blinked harder still as his eyes rested upon the portraits, and he secretly consulted the crumpled wine-card in his hand. Then he seemed to recover his breath by means of a profound sigh.

"Monsieur makes caricatures?" he inquired.

"Ah, monsieur," said Pierre, "at times, and for amusement only. I am a portraitist." And he pointed proudly to the picture against the wall.

For they are all alike, these painters—proudest of what they do least well!

"Ah, then," said Caffiard, with an air of resignation, "I must ask monsieur's pardon, and descend. I am not interested in portraits. When it comes to caricatures——"

"They are well enough in their way," put in Pierre, "but as a serious affair—to sell, for instance—well, monsieur comprehends that one does not debauch one's art!"

Oh, yes, they are all alike, these painters!

"What is serious, what is not serious?" answered Caffiard. "It is all a matter of opinion. One prefers to have his painting glued to the wall of the *Salon*, next the ceiling, another to have his drawing on the front page of *La Blague*."

"Oh, naturally *La Blague*," protested Pierre.

"I am its editor," said Caffiard superbly.

"*Eigh!*" exclaimed Pierre, for Mimi had cruelly pinched his arm. Before the sting had passed, she was seated at Caffiard's side, tugging at the strings of a great portfolio.

"Are they imbeciles, these painters, monsieur?" she was saying. "Now you shall see. This great baby is marvelous, but *marvelous* with his caricatures. Not Léandre himself— it is I who assure you, monsieur!—and to hear him, one would think—but thou *tirest* me, Pierrot!—With his portraits! No, it is *too* much!"

She spread the portfolio wide, and began to shuffle through the drawings it contained.

Caffiard's eyes glistened as he saw them. Even in her enthusiasm Mimi had not overshot the mark. They were marvelous indeed, these caricatures, mere outlines for the most part, with a dot, here and there, of red, or a little streak of green, which lent them a curious, unusual charm. The subjects were legion. Here was Loubet, with a great band of crimson across his shirt-bosom; here Waldeck-Rousseau, with eyes as round and prominent as agate marbles; or Yvette, with a nose on which one might have hung an overcoat; or Chamberlain, all monocle; or Wilhelmina, growing out of a tulip's heart, and as pretty as an old print, with her tight-fitting Dutch cap and broidered bodice. And then a host of types—cochers, grisettes, flower women, camelots, Heaven knows what not!—the products of half a hundred idle hours, wherein great-hearted, foolish Pierre had builded better than he knew!

Caffiard selected five at random, and then, from a waistcoat pocket that clung as closely to his round figure as if it had been glued thereto, produced a hundred-franc note.

"I must have these for *La Blague*, monsieur," he said.

"Bring me two caricatures a week at my office in the Rue St. Joseph, and you shall be paid at the same rate. It is not much, to be sure. But you will have ample time left for your—for your portrait-painting, monsieur!"

For a moment the words of Caffiard affected Pierre and Mimi as the stairs had affected Caffiard. They stared at him, opening and shutting their mouths and gasping, like fish newly landed. Then, suddenly, animated by a common impulse, they rushed into each other's arms, and set out, around the studio, in a mad waltz, which presently resolved itself into an impromptu can-can, with Mimi skipping like a fairy, and Pierre singing "Hi! *Hi! Hi!*" and snapping at her flying feet with a red-bordered handkerchief. After this Mimi kissed Caffiard twice: once on the top of his bald head, and once on the end of his stubby nose. It was like being brushed by the floating down of a dandelion. And, finally, nothing would do but that he must accompany them upon the morrow; and she explained to him in detail the plan which had so nearly fallen through, and the *deus ex machina* did not betray by so much as a wink that he had heard the entire story only half an hour before.

But, in the end, he protested. But she was insane, the little one, completely! Had he then the air of one who gave himself into those boats there, name of a pipe? But let us be reasonable, *voyons!* He was not young, like Pierre and Mimi; one comprehended that these holidays did not recommence when one was sixty. What should he do, he demanded of them, trailing along, as one might say, he and his odious fatness? Ah, *non!* For *la belle jeunesse* was *la belle jeunesse*, there was no means of denying it, and it was not for a species of dried sponge to be giving itself the airs of a fresh flower. "But no! But no!" said Caffiard, striving to rise from the divan. "In the morning I have my article to do for the *Figaro*, and I am going with

Caran to Longchamp, *en auto*, for the races in the afternoon. But no! But no!"

It was plain that Caffiard had known Mimi no more than half an hour. One never said, "But no! But no!" to Mimi, unless it was for the express purpose of having one's mouth covered by the softest little pink palm to be found between the Seine and the observatoire—which, to do him justice, Caffiard was quite capable of scheming to bring about, if only he had known! He had accepted the little dandelion-down kisses in a spirit of philosophy, knowing well that they were given not for his sake, but for Pierre's. But now his protests came to an abrupt termination, for Mimi suddenly seated herself on his lap, and put one arm around his neck.

It was nothing short of an achievement, this. Even Caffiard himself had not imagined that such a thing as his lap was still extant. Yet here was Mimi actually installed thereon, with her cheek pressed against his, and her breath, which was like clover, stirring the ends of his mustache. But she was smiling at Pierre, the witch! Caffiard could see it out of the corner of his eye.

"*Mais non!*" he repeated, but more feebly.

"*Mais non! Mais non! Mais non!*" mocked Mimi. "Great *farceur!* Will you listen, at least? *Eh b'en, voilà!* Here is my opinion. As to insanity, if for any one to propose a day in the country is insanity, well, then, yes—I am insane! *Soit!* And, again, if you wish to appear serious—in Paris, that is to say—*soit, également!* But when you speak of odious fatness, you are a type of monsieur extremely low of ceiling, do you know! Moreover, you are going. *Voilà!* It is finished. As for Caran, let him go his way and draw his caricatures— though they are not like Pierre's, all the world knows!—and without doubt his auto will refuse to move beyond the porte

Dauphine, yes, and blow up, *bon Dieu!* when he is in the act of mending it. One knows these boxes of vapors, what they do. And as for the *Figaro, b'en, flut!* Evidently it will not cease to exist for lack of your article—*eh, l'ami?* And it is Mimi who asks you—Mimi, do you understand, who invites you to her *fête.* And you would refuse her—*toi!*"

"But no! But no!" said Caffiard hurriedly. And meant it.

At this point Pierre wrapped five two-sou pieces in a bit of paper, and tossed them out of a little window across the hall-way, to a street-singer whimpering in the court below. Pierre said that they weighed down his pockets. They were in the way, the clumsy doublins, said wonderful, spendthrift Pierre!

For the wide sky of the Quartier is forever dotted with little clouds, scudding, scudding all day long. And when one of these passes across the sun, there is a sudden chill in the air, and one walks for a time in shadow, though the comrade over there, across the way, is still in the warm and golden glow. But when the sun has shouldered the little cloud aside again, ah, that is when life is good to live, and goes gaily, to the tinkle of glasses and the ripple of laughter and the ring of silver bits. And when the street-singer in the court receives upon his head a little parcel of coppers that are too heavy for the pocket, and smiles to himself, who knows but what he understands?

For what is also true of the Quartier is this—that, in sunshine or shadow, one finds a soft little hand clasping his, firm, warm, encouraging, and kindly, and hears a gay little voice that, in foul weather, chatters of the bright hours which it is so sweet to remember, and, in fair, says never a word of the storms which it is so easy to forget!

The veriest bat might have foreseen the end, when once Mimi had put her arm around the neck of Caffiard. Before the *deus ex machina* knew what he was about, he found his army of objections routed, horse, foot, and dragoons, and had promised to be at the gare St. Lazare at eleven the following morning.

And what a morning it was! Surely the *bon Dieu* must have loved Mimi an atom better than other mortals, for in the blue-black crucible of the night he fashioned a day as clear and glowing as a great jewel, and set it, blazing with warm light and vivid color, foremost in the diadem of the year. And it was something to see Mimi at the carriage-window, with Pierre at her side and her left hand in his, and in her right a huge bouquet—Caffiard's contribution; while the *deus ex machina* himself, breathing like a happy hippopotamus, beamed upon the pair from the opposite corner. So the train slipped past the fortifications, swung through a trim suburb, slid smoothly out into the open country. It was a Wednesday, and there was no holiday crowd to incommode them. They had the compartment to themselves; and the half-hour flew like six minutes, said Mimi, when at last they came to a shuddering standstill, and two guards hastened along the platform in opposite directions, one droning "Poiss-y-y-y-y!" and the other shouting "Poiss'! Poiss'! Poiss'!" as if he had been sneezing. It was an undertaking to get Caffiard out of the carriage, just as it had been to get him in. But finally it was accomplished, a whistle trilled from somewhere as if it had been a bird, another wailed like a stepped-on kitten, the locomotive squealed triumphantly, and the next minute the trio were alone in their glory.

It was a day that Caffiard never forgot. They breakfasted at once, so as to have a longer afternoon. Mimi was guide and commander-in-chief, as having been to the Esturgeon before, so the table was set upon the *terrasse* overlooking the Seine, and there were radishes, and little individual omelets, and a famous matelote, which Monsieur Jarry himself served with the air of a Lucullus, and, finally, a great dish of *quatre saisons*, and for each of the party a squat brown pot of fresh cream. And, moreover, no *ordinaire*, but St. Emilion, if you please, with a tin-foil cap which had to be removed before one could draw the cork, and a bottle of Source Badoit as well. And Caffiard, who had dined with the Russian Ambassador on Monday, and breakfasted with the Nuncio on Tuesday, and been egregiously displeased with the fare in both instances, consumed an unprecedented quantity of matelote, and went back to radishes after he had eaten his strawberries and cream; while, to cap the climax, Pierre paid the addition with a louis —and gave *all* the change as a tip! But it was unheard of!

Afterward they engaged a boat, and, with much alarm on the part of Mimi, and satirical comment from Caffiard, and severe admonitions to prudence by Pierre, pushed out into the stream and headed for Villennes, to the enormous edification of three small boys, who hung precariously over the railing of the terrace above them, and called Caffiard a captive balloon.

They made the three kilometers at a snail's pace, allowing the boat to drift with the current for an hour at a time, and now and again creeping in under the willows at the water's edge until they were wholly hidden from view, and the voice of Mimi singing was as that of some river nixie invisible to mortal eyes. She sang "Bonsoir, Madame la Lune," so sweetly and so sadly that Caffiard was moved to tears. It was her favorite song, because—oh, because it was about Pierrot! And her own Pierrot responded with a gay soldier ballad, a *chanson de route* which he had picked up at the Noctambules; and even Caffiard sang—a ridiculous ditty it was, which scored the English and went to a rollicking air. They all shouted the refrain, convulsed with merriment at the drollery of the sound:

> " *Qu'est ce qui quitte ses père et mère*
> *Afin de s'en aller*
> *S'faire taper dans le nez?*
> *C'est le soldat d'Angleterre!*
> *Dou-gle-di-gle-dum!*
> *Avec les ba-a-a-alles dum-dum!*"

Caffiard was to leave them at Villennes after they should have taken their *apéritifs*. They protested, stormed at him, scolded and cajoled by turns, and called him a score of fantastic names —for by this time they knew him intimately—as they sat in Monsieur Bodin's arbor and sipped amer-menthe, but all in vain. Pierre had Mimi's hand, as always, and he had kissed her a half-hundred times in the course of the afternoon. Mimi had a way of shaking her hair out of her eyes with a curious little backward jerk of her head when Pierre kissed her, and then looking at him seriously, seriously, but smiling when he caught her at it. Caffiard liked that. And Pierre had a trick of turning, as if to ask Mimi's opinion, or divine even her un-spoken wishes whenever a question came up for decision—a choice of food or drink, or direction, or what-not. And Caffiard liked *that*.

He looked across the table at them now, dreamily, through his cigarette smoke.

"Pierrot," he said, after he had persuaded them to let him depart in peace when the train should be due—"Pierrot. Yes, that is it. You, with your garret, and your painting, and your songs, and your black, black sadness at one moment, and your laughter the next, and, above all, your Pierrette, your *bon-bon* of a Pierrette—you are Pierrot, the spirit of Paris in powder and white muslin! Eigho! my children, what a thing it is, *la belle jeunesse! Tiens!* you have given me a taste of it to-day, and I thank you. I thought I had forgotten. But no, one never forgets. It all comes back—youth, and strength, and beauty, love, and music, and laughter—but only like a breath upon a mirror, my children, only like a wind-ripple on a pool; for I am an old man."

He paused, looking up at the vine-leaves on the trellis-roof, and murmured a few words of Mimi's song:

> *"Pierrette en songe va venir me voir:*
> *Bonsoir, madame la lune!"*

Then his eyes came back to her face.

"I must be off," he said. "Why, what hast thou, little one? There are tears in those two stars!"

"*C'est vrai?*" asked Mimi, smiling at him and then at Pierre, and brushing her hand across her eyes, "*c'est vrai?* Well, then, they are gone as quickly as they came. *Voilà!* Without his tears Pierrot is not Pierrot, and without Pierrot——"

She turned to Pierre suddenly, and buried her face on his shoulder.

"*Je t'aime!*" she whispered. "*Je t'aime!*"

—"*Zut and Other Parisians.*"

Josephine Dodge Daskam

The Woman Who Was Not Athletic

THERE was once a woman who wore High-heeled Shoes and a Tight Corset. Both These are Highly Injurious and Inartistic to the Last Degree. One Day she Went out to the Links with a Sensible Friend who wore a Sweater and Man-fashioned Shoes. There they Met Two Men playing Golf.

"I Fear I shall only Be in your Way," said the Woman who was Not Athletic. "I Cannot Play the Game. I do Not Know a Caddy from a Bunker, nor a Foursome from a Tee."

"Not at all. I will Describe the Game to You," said the Men.

"Oh, Thank You, but One will be Quite enough," she re-plied, and she Selected the Best-looking, and the Other Went out after the Sensible Friend.

"May I Carry your Parasol?" said he when they had Started.

"If you will Be so Good," she answered. "It is very Foolish, I know, but my Skin is so Absurdly Thin, and the Sun Blisters it so."

The Sensible Friend came up just Behind, and Mopping her Face, she said: "You are too Ridiculous. A Rose-colored Parasol on the Links! You are keeping Him from playing too. He will get Out of Practise."

"Oh, I Hope not," said the Woman who was Not Athletic.

"Do not be Alarmed," said the man. "It is All Right."

"Moreover, I saw him Help you Over a Fence," said the Sensible Friend, as she Waded through a Muddy Brook. "That Game is Out of Date."

The Woman who was Not Athletic looked Pensively and for Some Time at the Man.

"I am Spoiling Everything," she said softly. "Let me Go Home, and then You can Play."

"But then You could not Learn the Game," said he, Sitting down under a Kind of Artificial Watershed and Watching the Rose-colored Reflection of her Parasol.

"Is this a Bunker?" she asked.

"Yes," he replied. "Its Purpose is to shield People Who wish to be Alone, from Observation."

"Oh!" said she. "Then What is a Hazard?"

"Well," he replied, "this is sometimes Called a Hazard, too, because There is a Chance that Some one may Come By after all."

"Oh!" said she. "Then over That Wall Behind that Big Rock is one of the Best Bunkers on the Links, isn't it?"

"It is, indeed," he replied. "You Pick Up the Game very Rapidly. Come over There, and I will Explain it Further to You."

"You are so Good," she said, as he Lifted her Over the Wall.

"Not at All," he replied Politely.

Some Time Afterward the Sensible Friend, who was Engaged in Wallowing Through some Underbrush and Falling into a Pond in Search of Her Ball, Passed by Them on the Return Course, and Seeing them Seated against the Wall, noted their somewhat Unoriginal Attitudes. She was surprised.

This teaches us that You need Not Teach an Old Dog New Tricks.—*From Josephine Dodge Daskam's "Fables for the Fair," copyright by Charles Scribner's Sons.*

The Woman Who Used Her Theory

THERE was once a Woman who had a Theory that Men did Not Care for Too Much Intellectuality in her Sex. After this Theory she shaped her Actions, which Shows her to have been a Remarkable Woman. One day a Man asked her if she Belonged to his Sister's Ibsen Club.

"Oh, no," she answered; "I Cannot understand Ibsen at all."

The Next Time he called he brought her a Bunch of Violets and asked her if she read Maeterlinck.

"No; I think it is Very Silly," she replied.

Then the Man brought her a Box of Chocolates, remarking, "'Sweets to the Sweet'—do you not think Shakespeare was Right?"

The Woman saw that she was Making Progress. Now was her Time to Stop, but this she Did Not Perceive.

"Shakespeare?" said she. "Oh, yes, I have read a little of His Works, but I do not see Much Sense in them, to tell the Truth."

"Nay, nay," said the Man, "this is Too Much. Not to Understand Ibsen, shows that you are a Good Woman; to think Maeterlinck Silly, augurs Well for your Intelligence; but not to see Much Sense in Shakespeare, implies that you are Uneducated."

And he did not Call Again.

This teaches us that it is Possible to Get Too Much of a Good Thing.—*From Josephine Dodge Daskam's "Fables for the Fair," copyright by Charles Scribner's Sons.*

Josephine Dodge Daskam

The Woman Who Helped Her Sister

THERE was once a Woman who had Read in a Book that the Best Way to Become Dear to a Man was to Cook appetizing Dishes for Him. Therefore when a Nice Man Called on Her it was Her Custom to Retire to the Dining-room and Compose Delicious Lunches in a Chafing-dish, leaving her Sister to Entertain the Man till her return. Her Sister would not Learn to Cook, because she did Not Care to.

One Day the Man invited the Woman to Go to the Theater with him. This she would have Liked to do Very Much, but she Remembered What she had Read, and replied:

"I will Tell you Something Better. Take my Sister to the Theater, and when you Come Home I will have a Nice Supper waiting For You."

"Oh, very Well!" said the Man. That evening he Fell in Love with the Sister, and Some Time Later he asked her to Marry him.

"But I Thought it was My Sister you Came to See," said she; "and besides that, I Fear I should Make a Poor Wife. I am Not Practical, and I Cannot Cook."

"As to that," replied the Man, "I came at First, it is True, to see Your Sister, but I saw Very Little of her because she Stayed in the Dining-room So Much; so that I Grew to Admire You. And as for your Not Cooking, that is Easily Arranged. Your Sister can Live with Us and Manage All That very nicely."

This teaches us that you must Catch your Hare before you Cook for Him.—*From Josephine Dodge Daskam's "Fables for the Fair," copyright by Charles Scribner's Sons.*

John Carver

Country Burial-Places

In passing through New England, a stranger will be struck with the variety, in taste and feeling, respecting burial-places. Here and there may be seen a solitary grave, in a desolate and dreary pasture-lot, and anon under the shade of some lone tree, the simple stone reared by affection to the memory of one known and loved by the humble fireside only. There, on that gentle elevation, sloping green and beautiful toward the south, is a family enclosure adorned with trees and filled with the graves of the household. How many breaking hearts have there left the loved till that bright morning! Here in this garden, beside the vine-covered arbor and amid the shrubbery which her own hand planted, is the monument to the faithful wife and loving mother. How appropriate! How beautiful! And to the old landholders of New England, what motive to hold sacred from the hand of lucre so strong as the ground loved by the living as the burial-place of *their* dead!

Apropos to burying in gardens, I heard a story of an old man who was bent on interring his wife in his garden, despite of the opposition of all his neighbors to his doing so. Indeed, the old fellow avowed this as his chief reason, and to all their entreaties and deprecations and earnest requests he still declared he would do it. Finding everything they could do to be of no avail, the people bethought themselves of a certain physician, who was said to have great influence over the old man, and who owned an orchard adjoining the very garden. So, going to him in a body, they besought him to attempt to change the determination of his obstinate friend. The doctor consented to do so, and went. After offering his condolence on the loss of his wife, and proffering any aid he might be able to render at the funeral, the doctor said, "I understand you intend to bury your deceased wife in your garden."

"Yes," answered the old man, "I do. And the more people object, the more I'm determined to do it!"

"Right!" replied the doctor, with an emphatic shake of the head, "Right! I applaud the deed. I'd bury her there, if I was you. The boys are always stealing the pears from my favorite tree that overhangs your garden, and by and by you'll die, Uncle Diddle, and they'll bury you there, too, and then I'm sure that the boys will never dare steal another pear."

"No! I'll be hanged if I bury her there," said the old man in great wrath. "I'll bury her in the graveyard."

New England can boast her beautiful places of sculpture, but as a common thing they are too much neglected, and attractive only to the lover of oddities and curious old epitaphs. Occasionally you may see a strangely shaped tomb, or, as in a well-known village, a knocker placed on the door of his family vault by some odd specimen of humanity. When asked the reason for doing so singular a thing, he gravely replied that "when the old gentleman should come to claim his own, the tenants might have the pleasure of saying, 'Not at home,' or of fleeing out of the back door."

In passing through these neglected grounds you will often find some touchingly beautiful scriptural allusion—some apt quotation, or some emblem so lovely and instructive that the memory of it will go with you for days. Here in a neglected spot and amid a cluster of raised stones is the grave of the stranger clergyman's child who died on its journey. The inscription is sweet when taken in connection with the portion of sacred history from which the quotation is made: "Is it well with the child? And she answered, It is well." Again, the only inscription is an emblem—a butterfly rising from the chrysalis. Glorious thought, embodied in emblem so singular! "Sown in corruption, raised in incorruption!"

Then come you to some strangely odd, as, for instance:

> "Here lies John Auricular,
> Who in the ways of the Lord walked perpendicular."

Again:

> "Many a cold wind o'er my body shall roll,
> While in Abraham's bosom I'm feasting my soul."

Appropriate certainly, as the grave was on a cold northeast slope of one of our bleak hills.

Again, a Dutchman's epitaph for his twin babes:

> "Here lies two babes, dead as two nits,
> Who shook to death mit ague fits;
> They was too good to live mit me,
> So God He took 'em to live mit He."

There is the grave of a young man who, dying suddenly, was eulogized with this strange aim at the sublime:

> "He lived,
> He died!"

Not a hundred miles from Boston is a gravestone the epitaph upon which, to all who knew the parties, borders strongly upon the burlesque. A widower who within a few months buried his wife and adopted daughter, the former of whom was all her life long a thorn in his flesh, and whose death could not but have been a relief, wrote thus: "They were lovely and beloved in their lives, and in death were not divided." Poor man! Well *he* knew how full of strife and sorrow an evil woman can make life! He was worn to a shadow before her death, and his hair was all gone. Many of the neighbors thought surely that *he* well knew what had become of it, especially as it disappeared by the handful. But the grave covers all faults; and those who knew her could only hope that she might rest from her labors and her works follow her!

On a low, sandy mound far down on the Cape rises a tall slate stone, with fitting emblems and epitaphs as follows:

> "Here lies Judy and John,
> That lovely pair;
> John was killed by a whale,
> And Judy sleeps here."

> —*"Sketches of New England."*

Sam Davis

The First Piano in a Mining-Camp

IN 1858 (it might have been five years earlier or later; this is not the history for the public schools) there was a little camp about ten miles from Pioche, occupied by upward of three hundred miners, every one of whom might have packed his prospecting implements and left for more inviting fields any time before sunset. When the day was over, these men did not rest from their labors, like the honest New England agriculturist, but sang, danced, gambled, and shot each other, as the mood seized them.

One evening the report spread along the main street (which was the only street) that three men had been killed at Silver Reef, and that the bodies were coming in. Presently a lumbering old conveyance labored up the hill, drawn by a couple of horses well worn out with their pull. The cart contained a good-sized box, and no sooner did its outlines become visible, through the glimmer of a stray light here and there, than it began to affect the idlers. Death always enforces respect, and even though no one had caught sight of the remains, the crowd gradually became subdued, and when the horses came to a standstill the cart was immediately surrounded. The driver, however, was not in the least impressed with the solemnity of his commission.

"All there?" asked one.

"Haven't examined. Guess so."

The driver filled his pipe, and lit it as he continued:

"Wish the bones and load had gone over the grade!"

A man who had been looking on stepped up to the man at once.

"I don't know who you have in that box, but if they happen to be any friends of mine I'll lay you alongside."

"We can mighty soon see," said the teamster coolly. "Just burst the lid off, and if they happen to be the men you want, I'm here."

The two looked at each other for a moment, and then the crowd gathered a little closer, anticipating trouble.

"I believe that dead men are entitled to good treatment, and when you talk about hoping to see corpses go over a bank, all I have to say is, that it will be better for you if the late lamented ain't my friends."

"We'll open the box. I don't take back what I've said, and if my language don't suit your ways of thinking, I guess I can stand it."

With these words the teamster began to pry up the lid. He got a board off, and then pulled out some rags. A strip of something dark, like rosewood, presented itself.

"Eastern coffins, by thunder!" said several, and the crowd looked quite astonished.

Some more boards flew up, and the man who was ready to defend his friends' memory shifted his weapon a little. The cool manner of the teamster had so irritated him that he had made up his mind to pull his weapon at the first sight of the dead, even if the deceased was his worst and oldest enemy. Presently the whole of the box-cover was off, and the teamster, clearing away the packing, revealed to the astonished group the top of something which puzzled all alike.

"Boys," said he, "this is a pianner."

A general shout of laughter went up, and the man who had

been so anxious to enforce respect for the dead muttered something about feeling dry, and the keeper of the nearest bar was several ounces better off by the time the boys had given the joke all the attention it called for.

Had a dozen dead men been in the box their presence in the camp could not have occasioned half the excitement that the arrival of that lonely piano caused. But the next morning it was known that the instrument was to grace a hurdy-gurdy saloon owned by Tom Goskin, the leading gambler in the place. It took nearly a week to get this wonder on its legs, and the owner was the proudest individual in the State. It rose gradually from a recumbent to an upright position amid a confusion of tongues, after the manner of the Tower of Babel.

Of course everybody knew just how such an instrument should be put up. One knew where the "off hind leg" should go, and another was posted on the "front piece."

Scores of men came to the place every day to assist.

"I'll put the bones in good order."

"If you want the wires tuned up, I'm the boy."

"I've got music to feed it for a month."

Another brought a pair of blankets for a cover, and all took the liveliest interest in it. It was at last in a condition for business.

"It's been showin' its teeth all the week. We'd like to have it spit out something."

Alas! there wasn't a man to be found who could play upon the instrument. Goskin began to realize that he had a losing speculation on his hands. He had a fiddler, and a Mexican who thrummed a guitar. A pianist would have made his orchestra complete. One day a three-card monte player told a friend confidentially that he could "knock any amount of music out of the piano, if he only had it alone a few hours, to get his hand in." This report spread about the camp, but on being questioned he vowed that he didn't know a note of music. It was noted, however, as a suspicious circumstance, that he often hung about the instrument, and looked upon it longingly, like a hungry man gloating over a beefsteak in a restaurant window. There was no doubt but that this man had music in his soul, perhaps in his fingers' ends, but did not dare to make trial of his strength after the rules of harmony had suffered so many years of neglect. So the fiddler kept on with his jigs, and the greasy Mexican pawed his discordant guitar, but no man had the nerve to touch the piano. There were doubtless scores of men in the camp who would have given ten ounces of gold-dust to have been half an hour alone with it, but every man's nerve shrank from the jeers which the crowd would shower upon him should his first attempt prove a failure. It got to be generally understood that the hand which first essayed to draw music from the keys must not slouch its work. . . .

It was Christmas eve, and Goskin, according to his custom, had decorated his gambling-hell with sprigs of mountain cedar and a shrub whose crimson berries did not seem a bad imitation of English holly. The piano was covered with evergreens, and all that was wanting to completely fill the cup of Goskin's contentment was a man to play the instrument.

"Christmas night, and no piano-pounder," he said. "This is a nice country for a Christian to live in."

Getting a piece of paper, he scrawled the words:

$20 Reward
To a Compitant Pianer Player

This he stuck up on the music-rack, and, though the inscription glared at the frequenters of the room until midnight, it failed to draw any musician from his shell.

So the merrymaking went on; the hilarity grew apace. Men danced and sang to the music of the squeaky fiddle and worn-out guitar as the jolly crowd within tried to drown the howling of the storm without. Suddenly they became aware of the presence of a white-haired man crouching near the fireplace. His garments—such as were left—were wet with melting snow, and he had a half-starved, half-crazed expression. He held his thin, trembling hands toward the fire, and the light of the blazing wood made them almost transparent. He looked about him once in a while as if in search of something, and his presence cast such a chill over the place that gradually the sound of the revelry was hushed, and it seemed that this waif of the storm had brought in with it all of the gloom and cold-ness of the warring elements. Goskin, mixing up a cup of hot egg-nog, advanced and remarked cheerily:

"Here, stranger, brace up! This is the real stuff."

The man drained the cup, smacked his lips, and seemed more at home.

"Been prospecting, eh? Out in the mountains—caught in the storm? Lively night, this!"

"Pretty bad," said the man.

"Must feel pretty dry?"

The man looked at his streaming clothes and laughed, as if Goskin's remark was a sarcasm.

"How long out?"

"Four days."

"Hungry?"

The man rose up and, walking over to the lunch-counter, fell to work upon some roast bear, devouring it like any wild animal would have done. As meat and drink and warmth began to permeate the stranger, he seemed to expand and lighten up. His features lost their pallor, and he grew more and more content with the idea that he was not in the grave. As he underwent these changes, the people about him got merrier and happier, and threw off the temporary feeling of depression which he had laid upon them.

"Do you always have your place decorated like this?" he finally asked of Goskin.

"This is Christmas eve," was the reply.

The stranger was startled.

"December 24th, sure enough."

"That's the way I put it up, pard."

"When I was in England I always kept Christmas. But I had forgotten that this was the night. I've been wandering about in the mountains until I've lost track of the feasts of the Church."

Presently his eye fell upon the piano.

"Where's the player?" he asked.

"Never had any," said Goskin, blushing at the expression.

"I used to play when I was young."

Goskin almost fainted at the admission.

"Stranger, do tackle it, and give us a tune! Nary man in this camp ever had the nerve to wrestle with that music-box." His pulse beat faster, for he feared that the man would refuse.

"I'll do the best I can," he said.

There was no stool, but seizing a candle-box, he drew it up and seated himself before the instrument. It only required a few seconds for a hush to come over the room.

"That old coon is going to give the thing a rattle."

The sight of a man at the piano was something so unusual that even the faro-dealer, who was about to take in a fifty-dol-

lar bet on the trey, paused, and did not reach for the money.
Men stopped drinking, with the glasses at their lips. Conversation appeared to have been struck with a sort of paralysis, and
cards were no longer shuffled.

The old man brushed back his long white locks, looked up
to the ceiling, half closed his eyes, and in a mystic sort of reverie
passed his fingers over the keys. He touched but a single
note, yet the sound thrilled the room. It was the key to his
improvisation, and as he wove his chords together the music
laid its spell upon every ear and heart. He felt his way along
the keys, like a man treading uncertain paths, but he gained
confidence as he progressed, and presently bent to his work
like a master. The instrument was not in exact tune, but the
ears of his audience, through long disuse, did not detect anything radically wrong. They heard a succession of grand
chords, a suggestion of paradise, melodies here and there, and
it was enough.

"See him counter with his left!" said an old rough, enraptured.

"He calls the turn every time on the upper end of the board,"
responded a man with a stack of chips in his hand.

The player wandered off into the old ballads they had heard
at home. All the sad and melancholy and touching songs,
that came up like dreams of childhood, this unknown player
drew from the keys. His hand kneaded their hearts like dough,
and squeezed out tears as from a wet sponge.

As the strains flowed one upon the other, the listeners saw
their homes of the long-ago reared again; they were playing
once more where the apple-blossoms sank through the soft
air to join the violets on the green turf of the old New England
States; they saw the glories of the Wisconsin maples and the
haze of the Indian summer blending their hues together; they

recalled the heather of Scottish hills, the white cliffs of Britain, and heard the sullen roar of the sea, as it beat upon their memories vaguely. Then came all the old Christmas carols, such as they had sung in church thirty years before; the subtile music that brings up the glimmer of wax tapers, the solemn shrines, the evergreen, holly, mistletoe, and surpliced choirs. Then the remorseless performer planted his final stab in every heart with "Home, Sweet Home."

When the player ceased, the crowd slunk away from him. There was no more revelry and devilment left in his audience. Each man wanted to sneak off to his cabin and write the old folks a letter. The day was breaking as the last man left the place, and the player, laying his head down on the piano, fell asleep.

"I say, pard," said Goskin, "don't you want a little rest?"

"I feel tired," the old man said. "Perhaps you'll let me rest here for the matter of a day or so."

He walked behind the bar, where some old blankets were lying, and stretched himself upon them.

"I feel pretty sick. I guess I won't last long. I've got a brother down in the ravine—his name's Driscoll. He don't know I'm here. Can you get him before morning? I'd like to see his face once before I die."

Goskin started up at the mention of the name. He knew Driscoll well.

"He your brother? I'll have him here in half an hour."

As Goskin dashed out into the storm the musician pressed his hand to his side and groaned. Goskin heard the word "Hurry!" and sped down the ravine to Driscoll's cabin. It was quite light in the room when the two men returned. Driscoll was pale as death.

"My God! I hope he's alive! I wronged him when we lived in England, twenty years ago."

They saw the old man had drawn the blankets over his face. The two stood a moment, awed by the thought that he might be dead. Goskin lifted the blanket and pulled it down astonished. There was no one there!

"Gone!" cried Driscoll wildly.

"Gone!" echoed Goskin, pulling out his cash-drawer. "Ten thousand dollars in the sack, and the Lord knows how much loose change in the drawer!"

The next day the boys got out, followed a horse's tracks through the snow, and lost them in the trail leading toward Pioche.

There was a man missing from the camp. It was the three-card monte man, who used to deny pointblank that he could play the scale. One day they found a wig of white hair, and called to mind when the "stranger" had pushed those locks back when he looked toward the ceiling for inspiration, on the night of December 24, 1858.

Simeon Ford

The Discomforts of Travel

IT is conceded that there is nothing more educating and refining than travel. It is also conceded that nothing is more conducive to travel than free passes. You can now understand why I am so highly educated and so refined.

I know of nothing which so enhances the pleasure of a railroad trip as a pass. It smooths out all the asperities and fatigues of the journey. "It maketh glad the wilderness and the solitary places, and maketh the desert to rejoice and blossom as the rose." I have often risen up and left a comfortable fireside, kind friends, and solicitous creditors, and journeyed to remote and cheerless localities in which I was quite uninterested, lured thereto by the magic influence of a pass. You all know how Svengali hypnotized poor Trilby, simply by a few passes.

The immortal poet Longfellow was 'way off when he wrote:

"Try not the pass," the old man said;
"Dark lowers the tempest overhead;
 The roaring torrent is deep and wide."
And loud that clarion voice replied,
 "Excelsior."

Now, the old man probably advised the youth not to try the pass, because he knew, if he did, and got one, he would never be asked to pay fare again without feeling that an outrage was being perpetrated on him. The opium habit is a positive virtue compared with the pass habit. The fact that one is in no way entitled to free transportation only stimulates one in the desire to ride at some other fellow's expense.

One of the most dangerous laws we have is the one forbidding office-holders to accept passes. It keeps our leading citizens out of politics. Some one said (in a moment of temporary aberration of mind) that he'd "rather be right than President"; but I'd rather have an annual on the New York Central than be an Assemblyman in the tents of wickedness. (That's another biblical quotation.)

The only drawback about using a pass (in addition to the loss of your self-respect) is the harrowing thought, which constantly hovers over you, that in case of accident your mangled remains will be of no cash value to your afflicted family. It is a safe plan, when traveling on a pass, to spend a portion of your ill-gotten gains on an insurance policy. Then, in case of accident, your last moments will be soothed by the thought that you have beaten the game both ways.

But inasmuch as I have never succeeded in worming a pass out of the sleeping-car people, I feel at liberty to make a few remarks on that branch of the railroad service, not in a carping spirit, but more in sorrow than in anger.

It is frequently remarked (especially in advertisements) that travel in our palace cars is the acme of comfort and luxury; and I guess they are about as perfect as they can be made and still pay dividends on diluted stock; and yet, after a night in one, I always feel as if I had been through a severe attack of cholera infantum.

In winter, especially, the question of temperature is trying. The mercury, soon after you start, bounds up to one hundred and ten degrees in the shade. You endure this until you melt off several pounds of hard-earned flesh, and then you muster up courage to press the button. You "keep a-pushin' and a-shovin'" until you lay the foundation of a felon on the end of your finger, and finally the dusky Ethiopian reluctantly emerges from his place of concealment and gazes at you scornfully. You suggest that the temperature is all right for "India's coral strand," but is too ardent to be compatible with Jaeger hygienic underwear. Whereupon he removes the roof, sides, and bottom of the car, and the mercury falls to three below zero, while you sit there and freeze to death, not daring to again disturb him lest you sink still further in his estimation.

That night he gets square with you for your temerity by making up your berth last; and when, at 3 A.M., you finally retire, you wonder why you didn't sit up and doze, instead of going to bed to lie wide awake.

Some folks sleep in sleeping-cars—any one who has ears can swear to that—but I am not so gifted. I attribute this mainly to the blankets (so called). Bret Harte says a sleeping-car blanket is of the size and consistency of a cold buckwheat cake, and sets equally as well upon you. Certainly they are composed of some weird, uncanny substance, hot in summer, cold in winter, and maddening in spring and fall. For a man of three foot six they are of ample proportions; for a man six foot three they leave much to be desired; and the tall man is kept all night in suspense as to whether he had best pull up the blanket and freeze his feet, or pull it down and die of pneumonia.

And then the joy of getting your clothes on in the morning, especially in an upper berth! To balance yourself on the back of your neck, and while in this constrained attitude to adjust one's pants, without spilling out one's change or offending the lady in the adjoining section, requires gymnastic ability of no mean order. You are at liberty to vary this exercise, however, by lying on your stomach on the bottom of the car, and groping under the berth for your shoes, which the African potentate has, in the still watches of the night, smeared with blacking and artfully concealed.

But what a change comes o'er the dusky despot as you approach your destination! That frown, before which you have learned to tremble, is replaced by a smile of childlike blandness. His solicitation regarding your comfort during the last ten minutes of the journey is really touching. And when, at last, he draws his deadly whisk-broom upon you, all your resentment disappears, and you freely bestow upon him the money which you have been saving up to give your oldest daughter music-lessons.—*"A Few Remarks."*

At a Turkish Bath

GENTLE reader, have you ever bathed? Turkish bathed? I wot not. I have, wo is me, and I am now a sadder and a cleaner man. If this article, which is meant to be deliciously light and playful, appears to you to be fraught with an underlying varicose vein of gloom, do not hastily pass it by, but remember that it's in the interest of science. I have dallied with this luxury of the Orient (so called). Also remember that I have contracted a deep sonorous cold, which will, in all probability, fondly nestle in my bosom till my ulster blooms again.

The preliminaries of the Turkish bath are simple. You pay one dollar at the door, and pass into the "cooling-room," where the mercury registers ninety-eight degrees. The appropriateness of this title does not burst upon you until you have visited the inner shrine, where the temperature is up near the boiling-point. In the "cooling-room" you are privileged to deposit your valuables in a safe. I did not avail myself of this boon, however, for reasons of a purely private nature, but passed at once into the "disrobing-room." This room was not so large as to appear dreary, nor yet so small as some I have lodged in on the Bowery, but was about seven by four. The furniture was simple yet chaste, consisting of a chair, and a brush and comb long past their prime. The comb was chained to the wall, but the brush was permitted to roam at will. Hastily divesting myself of sealskins, Jaegers, and other panoplies of rank, I arranged them in a neat pile in the center of the room and placed the chair upon them. This simple precaution I had learned while occupying a room separated from its fellows by low partitions. Your neighbor may be a disciple of Izaak Walton, and during your sleep, or absence, may take a cast over the partition with hook and line. What could be more embarrassing than to have one's trousers thus surreptitiously removed! I am a lover of the "gentle art" myself, but I am ever loath to be played for a sucker.

I was now ushered into the "hot room," where a number of gentlemen were lolling about and perspiring affably and fluently. Being of a timid, shrinking nature, I was somewhat embarrassed on entering a room thus filled with strangers, and the more so as I realized that my costume was too bizarre and striking for one of my willowy proportions. So I flung myself with an affectation of easy grace upon a marble divan, but immediately arose therefrom with a vivid blush and a large blister. I then sat upon a seething chair until I came to a boil, when I rose up and endeavored to alleviate my sufferings by restlessly pacing the room. A few towels were scattered about, and as the nimble chamois leaps from crag to crag, so leaped I from towel to towel in my efforts to keep my feet off the red-hot floor.

Having basked in this room until I was quite aglow, I summoned the attendant and told him he could take me out at once, or wait yet a little longer and remove me through a hose. I then passed into the "manipulating-room," where I was laid out on an unelastic marble slab like a "found drowned" at the Morgue, and was taken in hand by a muscular attendant, who proceeded to manipulate me with great violence. He began upon my chest, upon which he pressed until he lifted his feet off the floor and my shoulder-blades made dents in the marble. I mildly asked if it was absolutely necessary that my respiratory organs should thus be flattened, to which he replied with a rich Turkish accent, "Come off, young feller! I know my biz," and swooped down upon my digestive organs. Manipulation consists of disjointing, dismembering, bruising, and rending limb from limb, and may be healthful, but it is not popular with me. This man said he was a pianist also, and that he could manipulate and at the same time strengthen his fingers and improve his technique; and to illustrate, he struck a few resounding chords in the small of my back, and then proceeded to interpret Wagner up and down my vertebræ, running scales, twiddling up in the treble and thundering down in the bass, just as if I were the keyboard of a Steinway grand—an illusion doubtless heightened by the ivory whiteness of my skin. He wound up by playing that grand show-off piece, the "Battle of Prague," while I joined in with the "Cries of the Wounded." It was a fine rendering, no doubt, but next time I am to be played upon I shall ask for a soft andante movement—a Chopin nocturne, say.—*"A Few Remarks."*

Simeon Ford

A Gentle Complaint

FAIRFIELD, CONN.

P. T. BARNUM, ESQ.

DEAR SIR: We have a large soiled Asiatic elephant visiting us now, which we suspect belongs to you. His skin is a misfit, and he keeps moving his trunk from side to side nervously. If you have missed an elephant answering to this description, please come up and take him away, as we have no use for him. An elephant on a place so small as ours is more of a trouble than a convenience. I have endeavored to frighten him away, but he does not seem at all timid, and my wife and I, assisted by our hired man, tried to push him out of the yard, but our efforts were unavailing. He has made our home his own now for some days, and he has become quite *de trop*. We do not mind him so much in the daytime, for he then basks mostly on the lawn and plays with the children (to whom he has greatly endeared himself), but at night he comes up and lays his head on our piazza, and his deep and stentorous breathing keeps my wife awake. I feel as though I were entitled to some compensation for his keep. He is a large though not fastidious eater, and he has destroyed some of my plants by treading on them; and he also leaned against our wood-house. My neighbor—who is something of a wag—says I have a lien on his trunk for the amount of his board; but that, of course, is only pleasantry. Your immediate attention will oblige

SIMEON FORD.
--*"A Few Remarks."*

Boyhood in a New England Hotel

I was raised in the State of Connecticut, but it was no fault of mine. My parents, before I reached the age of consent, experienced one of those sudden reverses of fortune which have always been so popular in my family, and we left our beautiful New York home, replete as it was with every luxury, including a large and variegated assortment of chattel mortgages, and moved up into Windham County, right in the center of the pie-belt and quite near the jumping-off place. It was a lovely, beautiful, quiet, peaceful, restful, healthful, desirable, bucolic hamlet, three miles from the cars and far, far from the madding throng, and where a man could use his knife for the purpose of transferring nourishment to his mouth without attracting undue attention. When I say it was quiet I but feebly describe it, but when I say it was healthful I am well within the mark. If a man died in that village under eighty years of age, they hung white crape on the door-bell and carved a little lamb on his tombstone. I left there twenty-five years ago to seek my fortune—which I'm still seeking—but the old people who were old then don't seem any older now. Last summer, when I went up with my children, I noticed that the same old people were about as lively as ever, and the same old pink pop-corn balls and jack-knives were still in the show-case of the store which I used to think I'd buy when I got rich, but no longer seem to crave.

We boarded at the village hotel, and the experience I gained there has been of incalculable advantage to me in later years. Whenever a knotty question of hotel ethics presents itself to me, I try and decide what my old landlord would have done, and then I do just the opposite.

And yet he had some good practical ideas, which I should like to adopt in my hotel. For instance, he expected his guests to saw and split their own fire-wood in winter, generously supplying the cord-wood, however, and the ax as well, and also the saw. If I remember aright, we were expected to supply the pork wherewith to grease the saw, but he furnished the saw. My room was in the third story, and its ceiling slanted down rapidly, so that sometimes in the night, when aroused by a rat bounding joyously around on the quilt, I would sit up suddenly and embed portions of my intellect in the rafters. In the midst of the room was a sheet-iron stove, of forbidding aspect, which stood like a lighthouse sequestered in the midst of a great arctic sea of zinc. It had great powers as a fuel-consumer, the peculiar quality so characteristic of country stoves, to wit, the more fire you had in the stove the colder the room seemed to become. I made a scientific examination of that stove, and conclusively demonstrated that of the heat generated thereby, one hundred and twenty-five per cent. went up the flue and the balance went into the formation of rheumatism, goose-flesh, and chilblains.

Being naturally of a somewhat shiftless nature, I very rarely laid in a stock of wood at night, and in consequence I frequently had to go down early of a winter morning and dally with that wood-pile. There are a good many cold things in this world—cold hands, cold feet, cold bottles, marble hearts, and frozen faces—but of all cold things in this world, the coldest is an ax helve which has reposed all of a winter's night on a Connecticut wood-pile.

There was another feature of this little hotel which commended itself to me. The food was good, plentiful, and nutritious, and it was all put on the table at once. The boarders were privileged to reach out and spear such viands as attracted their fancy, and transfer the same to their plates without loss of time. Compared with this Jeffersonian simplicity of service the average banquet seems cumbrous and ornate. Yet one thing is certain: things seemed to taste better in those days. Why, I can remember the thrill of ecstasy which vibrated through my Gothic system when the sound of the dinner-bell fell upon my strained and listening ear. With what mad haste I dashed up to the good old colonial wash-stand that stood near the door, dipped out a tin basinful of water, scooped up a handful of soft-soap out of the half-cocoanut, and proceeded to remove my disguise. And then the towel! Ah, me, the towel! It was a red-letter day in the history of that hotel when we got a clean towel. And then the comb and brush! Perhaps I ought to draw the veil of charity over the comb and brush; and yet I used them just as generations had done before me, and generations then unborn are doing yet. And when at last, with the mysteries of the toilet completed, with shining face and slicked hair, I would descend upon the dining-room and proceed to devastate the eatables—shades of Lucullus, Harvey Parker and Delmonico, how I did relish my victuals in those days!

Jarvis Keiley

The Song of the Jellyfish

As the waves slip over my cuticle sleek,
    They tickle my soul with glee,
And I shake with a visceral, saccharine joy,
    In the place where my ribs should be.
        For I'm simply a lump of limpid lard,
            With a gluey sort of a wish
        To pass my time in the oozing slime—
            In the home of the jellyfish.

But I'm happy in having no bones to break
    In my unctuous, wavering form,
And I haven't a trace, nor, indeed, any place,
    For the dangerous vermiform.
        For I'm built on the strictest economy plan,
            And the model was made in a rush,
        While essaying to think almost drives me to drink,
            For I'm simply a mass of mush.

At night, when I slide on the sandy beach,
    And the moonbeams pierce me through,
The tears arise in my gelatine eyes,
    And I gurgle a sob or two.
        For I wonder—ah, me!—in the time to come,
            When the days are no longer young,
        What fish's digestion will suffer congestion
            When the end of my song is sung.

Andrew V. Kelley—"Parmenas Mix"

He Came to Pay

THE editor sat with his head in his hands
    And his elbows at rest on his knees;
He was tired of the ever-increasing demands
    On his time, and he panted for ease.
The clamor for copy was scorned with a sneer,
    And he sighed in the lowest of tones:
"Won't somebody come with a dollar to cheer
    The heart of Emanuel Jones?"

Just then on the stairway a footstep was heard,
    And a rap-a-tap loud at the door,
And the flickering hope that had been long deferred
    Blazed up like a beacon once more;
And there entered a man with a cynical smile
    That was fringed with a stubble of red,
Who remarked, as he tilted a sorry old tile
    To the back of an average head:

"I have come here to pay." Here the editor cried
    "You're as welcome as flowers in spring!
Sit down in this easy armchair by my side,
    And excuse me a while till I bring
A lemonade dashed with a little old wine,
    And a dozen cigars of the best. . . .
Ah! Here we are! This, I assure you, is fine.
    Help yourself, most desirable guest."

Andrew V. Kelley

The visitor drank with a relish, and smoked
  Till his face wore a satisfied glow,
And the editor, beaming with merriment, joked
  In a joyous, spontaneous flow;
And then, when the stock of refreshments was gone,
  His guest took occasion to say,
In accents distorted somewhat by a yawn,
  "My errand up here is to pay——"

But the generous scribe, with a wave of his hand,
  Put a stop to the speech of his guest,
And brought in a melon, the finest the land
  Ever bore on its generous breast.
And the visitor, wearing a singular grin,
  Seized the heaviest half of the fruit,
And the juice, as it ran in a stream from his chin,
  Washed the mud of the pike from his boot.

Then, mopping his face on a favorite sheet
  Which the scribe had laid carefully by,
The visitor lazily rose to his feet
  With the dreariest kind of a sigh,
And he said, as the editor sought his address
  In his books, to discover his due:
"I came here to pay—my respects to the press,
And to borrow a dollar of you!"

Ben King

The Pessimist

NOTHING to do but work;
  Nothing to eat but food;
Nothing to wear but clothes,
  To keep one from going nude.

Nothing to breathe but air;
  Quick as a flash 'tis gone;
Nowhere to fall but off;
  Nowhere to stand but on.

Nothing to comb but hair;
  Nowhere to sleep but in bed;
Nothing to weep but tears;
  Nothing to bury but dead.

Nothing to sing but songs,
  Ah, well, alas! alack!
Nowhere to go but out;
  Nowhere to come but back.

Nothing to see but sights;
  Nothing to quench but thirst;
Nothing to have but what we've got;
  Thus thro' life we are cursed.

Sometimes published under the title "The Sum of Life."—EDITOR.

146

Ben King

Nothing to strike but a gait;
　　Everything moves that goes.
Nothing at all but common sense
　　Can ever withstand these woes.

If I Should Die To-Night

　　If I should die to-night,
And you should come to my cold corpse and say,
Weeping and heartsick o'er my lifeless clay—
　　If I should die to-night,
And you should come in deepest grief and wo—
And say, "Here's that ten dollars that I owe,"
　　I might arise in my large white cravat,
　　And say, "What's that?"

　　If I should die to-night,
And you should come to my cold corpse and kneel,
Clasping my bier to show the grief you feel,
　　I say, if I should die to-night,
And you should come to me, and there and then
Just even hint 'bout payin' me that ten,
　　I might arise the while,
　　But I'd drop dead again.

William J. Kountz, Jr.—"Billy Baxter"

In Society

PITTSBURG, PA., February 1, 1899.

DEAR JIM: There is no new scandal worth mentioning. What I started to write you about was Hemingway's duplicate whist party which was pulled off last night. I had a bid, and as there was nothing else stirring, I put on that boy's-size dress suit of mine and blew out there. Jim, you know the signs you see on the dummies in front of these little Yiddisher stores, "Take me home for $10.98," or "I used to be $6.21, now I'm yours for $3.39." Well, that's your Uncle Bill in a dress suit. Every one takes me for a waiter.

I have just been thinking this society push over, and I have come to the conclusion that an active leader in society has more troubles than a man in the wheat pit, and a man in the wheat pit is long on troubles about as often as he is on wheat. If you don't believe it, ask Joe Leiter. He was long on both at the same time.

Take the woman who uses fair English and has coin, and let her display the same good cold judgment that has made her husband successful in business, and some rainy Thursday morning the four hundred will wake up and find a new member has joined the order. While she is on her way she'll get many a frost, but after she lands she'll even up on the other candidates.

I have heard it said that locomotive engineers as a rule suffer from kidney troubles, caused by the jolting and bumping of the engine. If jolts and bumps go for anything, some of these

148

William J. Kountz, Jr.

people who are trying to break into society must have Bright's disease something grievous.

Jim, if you have never been to a duplicate whist party, see some of those people play whist and then order your shroud. Last night for a partner I drew an old girl who was a Colonial Dame because her ancestors on both sides had worked on the Old Colony Railroad. She must have taken a foolish powder or something, just before she left home, as she was clean to the bad. She had to be called five minutes before each play, and the way she trumped my ace the first time around was enough to drive a person dippy. Once she mentioned her husband's diamond-studded air-ship. Poor old lady! Probably took a double dose by mistake. How careless!

Everybody was making a great fuss over some girl who is lecturing throughout the country on "Man as Woman Sees Him." Talk about lavish eyes. My boy! my boy! but this dame was there with the swell lamps. A hundred candle-power easily. I tried to sit up to her, but there was nothing doing. I might have known I was a dead one. Because why? Because Mr. Percy Harold was talking to her, and he knows all about rare china, real old lace, and such things. When I came up the subject was Du Bois's "Messe de Mariage." (Spelling not guaranteed.) I asked about it this morning, Jim. A Messe de Mariage seems to be some kind of a wedding march, and a bishop who is a real hot dog won't issue a certificate unless the band plays the Messe. Mr. Percy Harold kept right on talking about Jack Hayes being so desperately in love with Mrs. Hardy-Steele, and how late they were getting home from the Opera the other night, and what a shame it was, as Mr. Steele seemed like such a nice fellow. There I stood like a Harlem goat. I couldn't cut in, because I have so many troubles of my own getting home from any place at all that I

149

haven't time to keep tab on other people. I must be as slow getting onto a scandal as the injured husband. If 15,000 people know something about a woman, my number is 14,999, and the husband's number is 15,000. It seems strange, but the husband always seems to get wise last.

But to return to the girl with the electric eyes. I hung around in that sad dress suit like a big dub, hoping that the conversation would finally get switched to theaters or dogs or sparring or something where I could make good; but Mr. Harold had the floor, and he certainly had me looking like a dirty deuce in a new deck. I stood for him till he suddenly exclaimed "Oh, fudge!" because he had forgotten one of his rings, and there was where I took to the tall timbers. If I were a ring I wouldn't let a guy like that wear me. Now, will you kindly tell me why it is that a girl will throw a good fellow down every time for one of those Lizzie boys? If I thought there were enough men in the country who feel as I do, I would start "The American Union for the Suppression of Lizzie Boys."

Well, I decided to git into my class, so I started for the smoking-room. I hadn't gone three feet till some woman held me up and began telling me how she adored grand opera. I didn't even reply. I flew madly, and remained hidden in the tall grasses of the smoking-room until it was time to go home. Jim, should any one ever tell you that grand opera is all right, he is either trying to even up, or he is not a true friend. I was over in New York with the family last winter, and they made me go with them to "Die Walküre" at the Metropolitan Opera House. When I got the tickets I asked the man's advice as to the best location. He said that all true lovers of music occupied the dress-circle and balconies, and that he had some good center dress-circle seats at three bones per. Here's a tip, Jim. If the box man ever hands you that true-lover game, just reach in through the little hole and soak him in the solar for me. It's coming to him. I'll give you my word of honor we were a quarter of a mile from the stage. We went up in an elevator, were shown to our seats, and who was right behind us but my old pal, Bud Hathaway, from Chicago. Bud had his two sisters with him, and he gave me one sad look which said plainer than words, "So you're up against it, too, eh?" We introduced all hands around, and about nine o'clock the curtain went up. After we had waited fully ten minutes, out came a big, fat, greasy-looking dago with nothing on but a bear robe. He went over to the side of the stage and sat down on a bum rock. It was plainly to be seen, even from my true-lover's seat, that his bearlets was sorer than a dog about something. Presently in came a woman, and none of the true lovers seemed to know who she was. Some said it was Melba, others Nordica. Bud and I decided it was May Irwin. We were mistaken, though, as Irwin has this woman lashed to the mast at any time or place. As soon as Mike the Dago espied the dame it was all off. He rushed, and drove a straight-arm jab, which, had it reached, would have given him the purse. But Shifty Sadie wasn't there. She ducked, side-stepped, and landed a clever half-arm hook which seemed to stun the big fellow. They clenched and swayed back and forth, growling continually, while the orchestra played this trembly Eliza-crossing-the-ice music. Jim, I'm not swelling this a bit. On the level, it happened just as I write it. All of a sudden some one seemed to win. They broke away, and ran wildly to the front of the stage with their arms outstretched, yelling to beat three of a kind. The band cut loose something fierce. The leader tore out about nine dollars' worth of hair and acted generally as though he had bats in his belfry. I thought sure the place would be pinched. It reminded me of Thirsty Thornton's dance-hall out in Merrill, Wisconsin, when the Silent Swede used to start a general survival of the fittest every time Mamie the Mink danced twice in succession with the young fellow from Albany, whose father owned the big mill up Rough River. Of course this audience was perfectly orderly, and showed no intention whatever of cutting in, and there were no chairs or glasses in the air, but I am forced to admit that the opera had Thornton's faded for noise. I asked Bud what the trouble was, and he answered that I could search him. The audience apparently went wild. Everybody said "Simply sublime!" "Isn't it grand?" "Perfectly superb!" "Bravo!" etc., not because they really enjoyed it, but merely because they thought it was the proper thing to do. After that for three solid hours Rough House Mike and Shifty Sadie seemed to be apologizing to the audience for their disgraceful street brawl, which was honestly the only good thing in the show. Along about twelve o'clock I thought I would talk over old times with Bud, but when I turned his way I found my tried and trusty comrade "Asleep at the Switch."

At the finish the woman next to me, who seemed to be on, said that the main lady was dying. After it was too late, Mike seemed kind of sorry. He must have given her the knife, or the drops, because there wasn't a minute that he could look in on her according to the rules. He laid her out on the bum rock, they set off a lot of red fire for some unknown reason, and the curtain dropped at 12.25. Never again for my money. Far be it from me knocking, but any time I want noise I'll take to a boiler-shop or a Union Station where I can understand what's coming off. I'm for a good mother show. Do you remember "The White Slave," Jim? Well, that's me. Wasn't it immense where the main lady spurned the villain's gold, and exclaimed with flashing eye, "Rags are royal raiment when worn for virtue's sake"? Great!

"The White Slave" has "Die Walküre" beaten to a pulp, and they don't get to you for three cases gate money, either.

Say, Jim, if you ever happen to be hunting around for a real true old sport, don't overlook General Hemingway, last evening's host. When it comes to warm propositions he is certainly the bell-cow. They all follow him. He is one of those fat, bald-headed old boys who at one time has had the smallpox so badly that he looks as though he had lost a lot of settings out of his face. He hustled for about twenty years, harnessed up a bunch of money, and now his life is one continual crimson sunset. Some people know when they have enough, but when the old general has enough he doesn't know anything. Smoke up! Jim, I didn't get that one myself the first time I heard it. Every time the general gets lit up he places his arm around your shoulder, puts his face close to yours, blows ashes in your eyes, and tells you confidentially, so that every one in Texas can hear him, that he knew your father when the seat of his trousers was ragged and he didn't have one dollar to rub against another. I don't mind that so much, but every time he comes to a word with the letter *P* in it he spits all over a fellow. Why, the other night he was telling me about our newly acquired *P*ossessions, the *P*hilippines, being a land of *P*erpetual *P*lenty, and for a while I thought I was in the na-tatorium. Under the circumstances I don't know which would be more desirable, a plumber for the general or a mackintosh for myself.   Yours as ever,

                                    BILLY.

P. S.—Jim, you know those little white checks they issue in some bars and you pay at the cashier's desk? Well, one of the boys just telephoned me that he saw Johnny Black in a down-town place with a beautiful sosh on, and that he was eating his checks because he was broke. He had swallowed five checks amounting to $2.30 before the bartender tumbled. That's a new one on me, and it's all right. My! but that boy Johnny is a sincere drinker.

Danforth Marble

The Hoosier and the Salt-Pile

"I'm sorry," says Dan, as he knocked the ashes from his regalia, as he sat in a small crowd over a glass of sherry at Florence's, New York, one evening, "I'm sorry that the stages are disappearing so rapidly; I never enjoyed traveling so well as in the slow coaches. I've made a good many passages over the Alleghanies, and across Ohio, from Cleveland to Columbus and Cincinnati, all over the South, down East, and up North, in stages, and I generally had a good time.

"When I passed over from Cleveland to Cincinnati, the last time, in a stage, I met a queer crowd—such a *corps*, such a time you never did see. I never was better amused in my life. We had a good team—spanking horses, fine coaches, and one of them *drivers* you read of. Well, there was nine 'insiders,' and I don't believe there ever was a stageful of Christians ever started before so chuck-full of music.

"There was a beautiful young lady going to one of the Cincinnati academies; next to her sat a Jew pedler—for Cowes and a market; wedging him in was a dandy blackleg, with jewelry and chains around about his breast and neck—enough to hang him. There was myself and an old gentleman with large spectacles, gold-headed cane, and a jolly, soldering-iron-looking nose; by him was a circus-rider whose breath was enough to breed yaller fever, and could be felt just as easy as cotton velvet! A cross old woman came next, and whose *look* would have given any reasonable man the double-breasted blues before breakfast; alongside of her was a rale backwoods

155

preacher, with the biggest and ugliest mouth ever got up since the flood. He was flanked by the low comedian of the party, an Indiana Hoosier, 'gwine down to Orleans to get an army contract' to supply the forces then in Mexico with beef.

"We rolled along for some time; nobody seemed inclined to 'open.' The old aunty sot bolt upright, looking crab-apples and persimmons at the Hoosier and the preacher; the young lady dropped the green curtain of her bonnet over her pretty face, and leaned back in her seat to nod and dream over japonicas and jumbles, pantalets and poetry; the old gentleman, proprietor of the Bardolph 'nose,' looked out at the 'corduroy' and swashes; the gambler fell off into a doze, and the circus covey followed suit, leaving the preacher and me *vis-à-vis* and saying nothing to nobody. 'Indianny,' he stuck his mug out at the window and criticized the cattle we now and then passed. I was wishing somebody would give the conversation a start, when 'Indianny' made a break:

"'This ain't no great stock country,' says he to the old gentleman with the cane.

"'No, sir,' was the reply. 'There's very little grazing here; the range is nearly wore out.'

"Then there was nothing said again for some time. Bimeby the Hoosier opened again:

"'It's the d——dest place for 'simmon trees and turkey buzzards I ever did see!'

"The old gentleman with the cane didn't say nothing, and the preacher gave a long groan. The young lady smiled through her veil, and the old lady snapped her eyes and looked sideways at the speaker.

"'Don't make much beef here, I reckon,' says the Hoosier.

"'No,' says the gentleman.

"'Well, I don't see how in h—ll they all manage to get along in a country whar thar ain't no ranges and they don't make no beef. A man ain't considered worth a cuss in Indianny what hasn't got his brand on a hundred head.'

"'Yours is a great beef country, I believe,' says the old gentleman.

"'Well, sir, it ain't anything else. A man that's got sense enuff to foller his own cow-bell with us ain't in no danger of starvin'. I'm gwine down to Orleans to see if I can't git a contract out of Uncle Sam to feed the boys what's been lickin' them infernal Mexicans so bad. I s'pose you've seed them cussed lies what's been in the papers about the Indianny boys at Bony Visty.'

"'I've read some accounts of the battle,' says the old gentleman, 'that didn't give a very flattering account of the conduct of some of our troops.'

"With that the Indianny man went into a full explanation of the affair, and, gittin' warmed up as he went along, begun to cuss and swear like he'd been through a dozen campaigns himself. The old preacher listened to him with evident signs of displeasure, twistin' and groanin' till he couldn't stand it no longer.

"'My friend,' says he, 'you must excuse me, but your conversation would be a great deal more interesting to me—and I'm sure would please the company much better—if you wouldn't swear so terribly. It's very wrong to swear, and I hope you'll have respect for our feelin's, if you hain't no respect for your Maker.'

"If the Hoosier had been struck with thunder and lightnin' he couldn't have been more completely tuck aback. He shut his mouth right in the middle of what he was sayin' and looked at the preacher, while his face got as red as fire.

"'Swearin',' says the preacher, 'is a terrible bad practise, and there ain't no use in it nohow. The Bible says, "Swear not at all," and I s'pose you know the commandments about swearin'?'

"The old lady sort of brightened up—the preacher was her 'duck of a man'; the old fellow with the 'nose' and cane let off a few 'umph, ah! umphs.' But 'Indianny' kept shady; he appeared to be *cowed* down.

"'I know,' says the preacher, 'that a great many people swear without thinkin', and some people don't b'lieve the Bible.'

"And then he went on to preach a regular sermon agin swearing, and to quote Scripture like he had the whole Bible by heart. In the course of his argument he undertook to prove the Scrip-tures to be true, and told us all about the miracles and prophec es and their fulfilment. The old gentleman with the cane took a part in the conversation, and the Hoosier listened without ever opening his head.

"'I've just heard of a gentleman,' says the preacher, 'that's been to the Holy Land and went over the Bible country. It's astonishin' to hear what wonderful things he has seen. He was at Sodom and Gomorrow, and seen the place whar Lot's wife fell!'

"'Ah,' says the old gentleman with the cane.

"'Yes,' says the preacher, 'he went to the very spot; and what's the remarkablest thing of all, he seen the pillar of salt what she was turned into!'

"'Is it possible!' says the old gentleman.

"'Yes, sir; he seen the salt, standin' thar to this day.'

"'What!' says the Hoosier, 'real genewine, good salt?'

"'Yes, sir; a pillar of salt, jest as it was when that wicked woman was punished for her disobedience.'

"All but the gambler, who was snoozing in the corner of the coach, looked at the preacher—the Hoosier with an expression of countenance that plainly told that his mind was powerfully convicted of an important fact.

"'Right out in the open air?' he asked.

"'Yes, standin' right in the open field, whar she fell.'

"'Well, sir,' says 'Indianny,' 'all I've got to say is, *if she'd dropped in our parts, the cattle would have licked her up afore sundown!*'

"The preacher raised both his hands at such an irreverent remark, and the old gentleman laughed himself into a fit of asthmatics, what he didn't get over till he came to the next change of horses. The Hoosier had played the mischief with the gravity of the whole party; even the old maid had to put her handkerchief to her face, and the young lady's eyes were filled with tears for half an hour afterward. The old preacher hadn't another word to say on the subject; but whenever we came to any place or met anybody on the road, the circus man nursed the thing along by asking what was the price of salt."

Stephen Leacock

My Financial Career

WHEN I go into a bank I get rattled. The clerks rattle me; the wickets rattle me; the sight of the money rattles me; everything rattles me.

The moment I cross the threshold of a bank I am a hesitating jay. If I attempt to transact business there I become an irresponsible idiot.

I knew this beforehand, but my salary had been raised to fifty dollars a month, and I felt that the bank was the only place for it.

So I shambled in and looked timidly around at the clerks. I had an idea that a person about to open an account must needs consult the manager.

I went up to a wicket marked "Accountant." The accountant was a tall, cool devil. The very sight of him rattled me. My voice was sepulchral.

"Can I see the manager?" I said, and added solemnly, "alone." I don't know why I said "alone."

"Certainly," said the accountant, and fetched him.

The manager was a grave, calm man. I held my fifty-six dollars clutched in a crumpled ball in my pocket.

"Are you the manager?" I said. God knows I didn't doubt it.

"Yes," he said.

"Can I see you?" I asked. "Alone?" I didn't want to say "alone" again, but without it the thing seemed self-evident.

The manager looked at me in some alarm. He felt that I had an awful secret to reveal.

"Come in here," he said, and led the way to a private room. He turned the key.

"We are safe from interruption here," he said; "sit down."

We both sat down and looked at one another. I found no voice to speak.

"You are one of Pinkerton's men, I presume," he said.

He had gathered from my mysterious manner that I was a detective. I knew what he was thinking and it made me worse.

"No, not from Pinkerton's," I said, seemingly to imply that I came from a rival agency. "To tell the truth," I went on, as if I *had* been prompted to lie about it, "I am not a detective at all. I have come to open an account. I intend to keep all my money in this bank."

The manager looked relieved, but still serious; he concluded now that I was a son of Baron Rothschild, or a young Gould.

"A large account, I suppose," he said.

"Fairly large," I whispered. "I propose to deposit fifty-six dollars now, and fifty dollars a month regularly."

The manager got up and opened the door. He called to the accountant.

"Mr. Montgomery," he said, unkindly loud, "this gentleman is opening an account; he will deposit fifty-six dollars. Good morning."

I rose.

A big iron door stood open at the side of the room.

"Good morning," I said, and stepped into the safe.

"Come out," said the manager coldly, and showed me the other way.

I went up to the accountant's wicket and poked the ball of money at him with a quick, convulsive movement, as if I were doing a conjuring trick.

My face was ghastly pale.

"Here," I said, "deposit it." The tone of the words seemed to mean, "Let us do this painful thing while the fit is on us."

He took the money and gave it to another clerk. He made me write the sum on a slip and sign my name in a book. I no longer knew what I was doing. The bank swam before my eyes.

"Is it deposited?" I asked in a hollow vibrating voice.

"It is," said the accountant.

"Then I want to draw a check."

My idea was to draw out six dollars of it for present use. Some one gave me a check-book through a wicket, and some one else began telling me how to write it out. The people in the bank had the impression that I was an invalid millionaire. I wrote something on the check and thrust it in at the clerk. He looked at it.

"What! Are you drawing it all out again?" he asked in surprise. Then I realized that I had written fifty-six instead of six. I was too far gone to reason now. I had a feeling that it was impossible to explain the thing. All the clerks had stopped writing to look at me.

Reckless with misery, I made a plunge.

"Yes, the whole thing."

"You withdraw your money from the bank?"

"Every cent of it."

"Are you not going to deposit any more?" said the clerk, astonished.

"Never."

An idiot hope struck me that they might think something had insulted me while I was writing the check and that I had changed my mind. I made a wretched attempt to look like a man with a fearfully quick temper.

The clerk prepared to pay the money.

"How will you have it?" he said.

"What?"

"How will you have it?"

"Oh!" I caught his meaning, and answered, without even trying to think, "In fifties."

He gave me a fifty-dollar bill.

"And the six?" he asked dryly.

"In sixes," I said.

He gave it me, and I rushed out.

As the big doors swung behind me I caught the echo of a roar of laughter that went up to the ceiling of the bank. Since then I bank no more. I keep my money in cash in my trousers pocket, and my savings in silver dollars in a sock.

Joshua S. Morris

The Harp of a Thousand Strings

A Hard-Shell Baptist Sermon

(This characteristic effusion first appeared in a New Orleans paper. The sermon is supposed to have been preached at a village on the bank of the Mississippi River, whither the volunteer parson had brought his flatboat for the purpose of trade.)

I MAY say to you, my brethring, that I am not an edicated man, an' I am not one of them as beleeves that edication is necessary for a Gospel minister, for I beleeve the Lord edicates his preachers jest as He wants 'em to be edicated; an' although I say it that oughtn't to say it, yet in the State of Indianny, whar I live, thar's no man as gits bigger congregations nor what I gits.

Thar may be some here to-day, my brethring, as don't know what persuasion I am uv. Well, I must say to you, my brethring, that I'm a Hard-shell Baptist. Thar's some folks as don't like the Hard-shell Baptists, but I'd rather have a hard shell as no shell at all. You see me here to-day, my brethring, dressed up in fine clothes; you mout think I was proud, but I am not proud, my brethring; and although I've been a preacher of the Gospel for twenty years, an' although I'm capting of the flatboat that lies at your landing, I'm not proud, my brethring.

I am not gwine to tell edzactly whar my tex may be found; suffice to say, it's in the leds of the Bible, and you'll find it somewhar between the fust chapter of the book of Generations and

164

Joshua S. Morris

the last chapter of the book of Revolutions; and ef you'll go and search the Scriptures, you'll not only find my tex thar, but a great many other texes as will do you good to read; and my tex, when you shall find it, you shall find it to read thus:

"And he played on a harp uv a thousand strings, sperits uv jest men made perfeck."

My text, my brethring, leads me to speak of sperits. Now, thar's a great many kinds of sperits in the world. In the fust place, thar's the sperits as some folks call ghosts; and thar's the sperits of turpentine; and thar's the sperits as some folks call liquor, an' I've got as good an artikel of them kind of sperits on my flatboat as ever was fotch down the Mississippi River. But thar's a great many other kinds of sperits, for the tex says, "He played on a harp uv a *t-h-o-u-s*-and strings, sperits uv jest men made perfeck."

But I tell you the kind uv sperits is as meant in the tex is FIRE. That's the kind uv sperits as is meant in the tex, my brethring. Now, thar's a great many kinds of fire in the world. In the fust place, there's the common sort of fire you light your cigar or pipe with; and then thar's foxfire and camphire, fire before you're ready, and fire and fall back, and many other kinds of fire—for the tex says, "He played on a harp uv a *thous*and strings, sperits uv jest men made perfeck."

But I'll tell you the kind of fire is as meant in the tex, my brethring: it's HELL-FIRE! An' that's the kind uv fire as a great many uv you'll come to, ef you don't do better nor what you have been doin'—for "He played on a harp uv a *thous*and strings, sperits uv jest men made perfeck."

Now, the different sorts of fire in the world may be likened unto the different persuasions of Christians in the world. In the fust place, we have the Piscapalions, an' they are a high-

165

sailin' and highfalutin' set; and they may be likened unto a turkey buzzard that flies up into the air, and he goes up, and up, and up, till he looks no bigger than your finger-nail, and the fust thing you know, he cums down, and down, and down, and is a-fillin' himself on the carkiss of a dead hoss by the side of the road—and "He played on a harp uv a *thous*and strings, sperits uv jest men made perfeck."

And then thar's the Methodis, and they may be likened unto the squirril runnin' up into a tree, for the Methodis beleeves in gwine on from one degree of grace to another, and finally on to perfection; and the squirril goes up and up, and up and up, and he jumps from limb to limb, and branch to branch, and the fust thing you know he falls, and down he cums kerflumix; and that's like the Methodis, for they is allers fallin' from grace, ah!—and "He played on a harp uv a *thous*and strings, sperits uv jest men made perfeck."

And then, my brethring, thar's the Baptist, ah! and they have been likened unto a 'possum on a 'simmon tree, and thunders may roll and the earth may quake, but that 'possum clings thar still, ah! and you may shake one foot loose, and the other's thar, and you may shake all feet loose, and he laps his tail around the limb, and clings, and he clings furever— for "He played on a harp uv a *thous*and strings, sperits uv jest men made perfeck."

Ed Mott

The Old Settler

His Reasons for Thinking There is Natural Gas in Deep Rock Gully

"I SEE by the papers, squire," said the Old Settler, "that they're a-findin' signs o' coal-ile an' nat'ral gas like sixty here an' thar in deestricks not so terrible fur from here, an' th't konsekently land they usety beg folks to come an' take offen their hands at any price at all, is wuth a dollar now jist for a peep over the stun wall at it. The minute a feller finds signs o' ile or nat'ral gas on his plantation, he needn't lug home his supplies in a quart jug no more, but kin roll 'em in by the bar'l; fer signs o' them kind is wuth more an inch th'n a sartin-per-sure grass an' 'tater farm is wuth an acre."

"Guess ye're huggin' the truth pooty clus fer wunst, major," replied the squire, "but th' hain't none o' them signs ez likely to strike anywhar in our bailiwick ez lightnin' is to kill a crow roostin' on the North Pole. There's one thing I've alluz wanted to see," continued the squire, "but natur' has ben agin me an' I hain't never seen it, an' that thing is the h'istin' of a balloon. Th' can't be no balloon h'isted nowhar, I'm told, 'nless there's gas to h'ist it with. I s'pose if we'd ha' had gas here, a good many fellers with balloons'd ha' kim 'round this way an' showed us a balloon-raisin' ev'ry now an' then. Them must be lucky deestricks that's got gas, an' I'd like to hev somebody strike it 'round here some'rs, jist fer the sake o' havin' the chance to see a balloon h'istin' 'fore I turn my toes up. But that's 'bout ez liable to happen ez it is fer to go out an' find a silver dollar rollin' up hill an' my name gouged in it."

"Don't ye be so consarned sure o' that, squire," said the Old Settler mysteriously, and with a knowing shake of his head. "I've been a-thinkin' a leetle sence readin' 'bout them signs o' gas, b'gosh! I hain't been only thinkin', but I've been a-rec-ollectin', an' the chances is th't me an' you'll see wonders yet afore we paddle over Jurdan. I'm a-goin' ter tell ye fer w'y, but I hadn't orter, squire, an' if it wa'n't fer makin' ye 'shamed o' yerself, an' showin' th't truth squashed in the mud is bound to git up agin if ye give her time, I wouldn't do it. Ye mowt remember th't jist ten years ago this month I kim in from a leetle b'ar hunt. I didn't bring in no b'ar, but I fotched back an up-an'-up account o' how I had shot one, an' how th' were sumpin' fearful an' queer an' amazin' in the p'formances o' that b'ar arter bein' shot. Mebbe ye 'member me a-tellin' ye that story, squire, an' you a-tellin' me right in my teeth th't ye know'd th't some o' yer friends had took to lyin', but th't ye didn't think any of 'em had it so bad ez that. But I hain't a-holdin' no gredge, an' now I'll tell ye sumpin' that'll s'prise ye.

"Ez I tol' ye at the time, squire, I got the tip ten year ago this month, th't unless somebody went up to Steve Groner's hill place an' poured a pound or two o' lead inter a big b'ar th't had squatted on that farm, th't Steve wouldn't hev no live-stock left to pervide pork an' beef fer his winterin' over, even if he managed to keep hisself an' fam'ly theirselfs from linin' the b'ar's innards. I shouldered my gun an' went up to Steve's to hev some fun with bruin, an' to save Steve's stock and resky him an' his folks from the rampagin' b'ar.

"'He's a rip-snorter,' Steve says to me, w'en I got thar. 'He don't think nuthin' o' luggin' off a cow,' he says, 'an' ye don't wanter hev yer weather eye shet w'en you an' him comes together,' he says.

"'B'ars,' I says to Steve, 'b'ars is nuts fer me, an' the bigger

an' sassier they be,' I says, 'the more I inj'y 'em,' I says; an'
with that I clim' inter the woods to show bruin th't th' wa'n't
room enough here below fer me an' him both. 'Tain't necessary fer me to tell o' the half dozen or more lively skrimmages
me an' that b'ar had ez we follered an' chased one another
round an' round them woods; how he'd hid ahind some big
tree or stumps, an' ez I went by, climb onto me with all four
o' his feet, an' yank an' bite an' claw an' dig meat an' clothes
offen me till I slung him off an' made him skin away to save
his bacon; an' how I'd lay the same way fer him, an' w'en he
come sneakin' 'long arter me agin, pitch arter him like a mad
painter, an' swat an' pound an' choke an' rassel him till his
tongue hung out, till I were sorry for him, an' let him git away
inter the brush agin to recooperate fer the next round. 'Tain't
wuth w'ile fer me to say anything 'bout them little skrimmages
'cept the last un, an' that un wa'n't a skrimmage, but sumpin'
that'd 'a' skeert some folks dead in their tracks.

"Arter havin' a half a dozen or so o' rassels with this big
b'ar, jist fer fun, I made up my mind, ez 'twere gettin' late, an'
ez Steve Groner's folks was mebbe feelin' anxious to hear which
was goin' ter run the farm, them or the b'ar, th't the next heat
with bruin would be for keeps. I guess the ol' feller had made
up his mind the same way, fer w'en I run agin him the las' time,
he were riz up on his hind legs right on the edge o' Deep Rock
Gully, and were waitin' fer me with his jaws wide open. I
unslung my gun, an' takin' aim at one o' the b'ar's forepaws,
thought I'd wing him an' make him come away from the edge
o' the gully 'fore I tackled him. The ball hit the paw, an' the
b'ar throw'd 'em both up. But he throw'd 'em up too fur, an'
he fell over back'rd, an' went head foremost inter the gully.
Deep Rock Gully ain't an inch less'n fifty foot from top to
bottom, an' the walls is ez steep ez the side of a house. I

went up to the edge an' looked over. There were the b'ar
layin' on his face at the bottom, whar them queer cracks is in
the ground, an' he were a-howlin' like a hurricane and kickin'
like a mule. There he laid, and he wa'n't able to rise up.
Th' wa'n't no way o' gettin' down to him 'cept by tumblin'
down ez he hed, an' if ever anybody were poppin' mad I were,
ez I see my meat a-layin' at the bottom o' that gully, an' the
crows a-getherin' to hev a picnic with it. The more I kep' my
eyes on that b'ar the madder I got, an' I were jist about to roll
and tumble an' slide down the side o' that gully ruther than go
back home an' say th't I'd let the crows steal a b'ar away from
me, w'en I see a funny change comin' over the b'ar. He didn't
howl so much, an' his kicks wa'n't so vicious. Then his hind
parts began to lift themse'fs up offen the ground in a cur'ous
sort o' way, and swung an' bobbed in the air. They kep'
raisin' higher an' higher, till the b'ar were act'ally standin'
on his head, an' swayin' to and fro ez if a wind were blowin'
him an' he couldn't help it. The sight was so oncommon out
o' the reg'lar way b'ars has o' actin' that it seemed skeery, an'
I felt ez if I'd ruther be home diggin' my 'taters. But I kep'
on gazin' at the b'ar a-circusin' at the bottom o' the gully, and
'twa'n't long 'fore the hull big carcass begun to rise right up
offen the ground an' come a-floatin' up outen the gully, fer all
the world ez if 'twa'n't more'n a feather. The b'ar come
up'ard tail foremost, an' I noticed th't he looked consid'able
puffed out like, makin' him seem lik' a bar'l sailin' in the air.
Ez the b'ar kim a-floatin' out o' the dep's I could feel my eyes
begin to bulge, an' my knees to shake like a jumpin'-jack's.
But I couldn't move no more'n a stun wall kin, an' thar I stood
on the edge o' the gully, starin' at the b'ar ez it sailed on up to'rd
me. The b'ar were making a desperate effort to git itself back
to its nat'ral p'sition on all fours, but th' wa'n't no use, an'

up he sailed, tail foremost, an' lookin' ez if he were goin' ter bust the next minute, he were swelled out so. Ez the b'ar bobbed up and passed by me I could ha' reached out an' grabbed him by the paw, an' I think he wanted me to, the way he acted, but I couldn't ha' made a move to stop him, not if he'd ben my gran'mother. The b'ar sailed on above me, an' th' were a look in his eyes th't I won't never fergit. It was a skeert look, an' a look that seemed to say th't it were all my fault, an' th't I'd be sorry fer it some time. The b'ar squirmed an' struggled agin comin' to setch an' onheerd-on end, but up'ard he went, tail foremost, to'rd the clouds.

"I stood thar par'lyzed, w'ile the b'ar went up'ard. The crows that had been settlin' round in the trees, expectin' to hev a bully meal, went to flyin' an' scootin' around the onfortnit b'ar, an' yelled till I were durn nigh deef. It wa'n't until the b'ar had floated up nigh onto a hundred yards in the air, an' begun to look like a flyin' cub, that my senses kim back to me. Quick ez a flash I rammed a load inter my rifle, wrappin' the ball with a big piece o' dry linen, not havin' time to tear it to the right size. Then I took aim an' let her go. Fast ez that ball went, I could see that the linen round it had been sot on fire by the powder. The ball overtook the b'ar and bored a hole in his side. Then the funniest thing of all happened. A streak of fire a yard long shot out o' the b'ar's side where the bullet had gone in, an' ez long ez that poor bewitched b'ar were in sight—fer o' course I thort at the time th't the b'ar were bewitched—I could see that streak o' fire sailin' along in the sky till it went out at last like a shootin' star. I never knowed w'at become o' the b'ar, an' the hull thing were a startlin' myst'ry to me; but I kim home, squire, an' tol' ye the story, jest ez I've tol' ye now, an' ye were so durn polite th't ye said I were a liar. But sence, I've been a-thinkin' an' recollectin'.

Squire, I don't hold no gredge. The myst'ry's plain ez day, now. We don't want no better signs o' gas th'n that, do we, squire?"

"Than what?" said the squire.

"Than what!" exclaimed the Old Settler. "Than that b'ar, o' course! That's w'at ailed him. It's plain enough th't there's nat'ral gas on the Groner place, an' th't it leaks outen the ground in Deep Rock Gully. W'en that b'ar tumbled to the bottom that day, he fell on his face. He were hurt so th't he couldn't get up. O' course the gas didn't shut itself off, but kep' on a-leakin', an' shot up inter the b'ar's mouth and down his throat. The onfortnit b'ar couldn't help hisself, an' bimeby he were filled with gas like a balloon, till he had to float, an' away he sailed, up an' up an' up. W'en I fired at the b'ar, ez he was floatin' to'ard the clouds, the linen on the bullet carried fire with it, and w'en the bullet tapped the b'ar's side the burnin' linen sot it on fire, showin' th't th' can't be no doubt 'bout it bein' gas th't the b'ar swallered in Deep Rock Gully. So ye see, squire, I wa'n't no liar, an' the chances is all in favor o' your seein' a balloon h'isted from gas right in yer own baili- wick afore ye turn up yer toes."

The squire gazed at the Old Settler in silent amazement for a minute or more. Then he threw up his hands, and said:

"Wal—I'll—be—durned!"

Mary N. Murfree—"Charles Egbert Craddock"

Borrowing a Hammer

On a certain bold crag that juts far over a steep wooded mountain-slope a red light was seen one moonless night in June. Sometimes it glowed intensely among the gray mists which hovered above the deep and somber valley; sometimes it faded. Its life was the breath of the bellows, for a blacksmith's shop stands close beside the road that rambles along the brink of the mountain. Generally after sunset the forge is dark and silent. So when three small boys, approaching the log hut through the gloomy woods, heard the clink! clank! clink! clank! of the hammers, and the metallic echo among the cliffs, they stopped short in astonishment.

"Thar, now!" exclaimed Abner Ryder desperately; "dad's at it fer true!"

"Mebbe he'll go away arter a while, Ab," suggested Jim Gryce, another of the small boys. "Then that'll gin us our chance."

"Waal, I reckon we kin stiffen up our hearts ter wait," said Ab resignedly.

All three sat down on a log a short distance from the shop, and presently they became so engrossed in their talk that they did not notice when the blacksmith, in the pauses of his work, came to the door for a breath of air. They failed to discreetly lower their voices, and thus they had a listener on whose attention they had not counted.

"Ye see," observed Ab in a high, shrill pipe, "dad sets a

heap o' store by his tools. But dad, ye know, air a mighty slack-twisted man. He gits his tools lost" (reprehensively), "he wastes his nails, an' then he 'lows ez how it war *me* ez done it."

He paused impressively in virtuous indignation. A murmur of surprise and sympathy rose from his companions. Then he recommenced:

"Dad air the crankiest man on this hyar mounting! He won't lend me none o' his tools nowadays—not even that thar leetle hammer o' his'n. An' I'm obleeged ter hev that thar leetle hammer an' some nails ter fix a box fer them young squir'ls what we cotched. So we'll jes' hev ter go ter his shop of a night when he is away, an'—an'—an' borry it!"

The blacksmith, a tall, powerfully built man, of an aspect far from jocular, leaned slightly out of the door, peering in the direction where the three tow-headed urchins waited. Then he glanced within at a leather strap, as if he appreciated the appropriateness of an intimate relation between these objects. But there was no time for pleasure now. He was back in his shop in a moment.

His next respite was thus entertained:

"What makes him work so of a night?" asked Jim Gryce.

"Waal," explained Ab in his usual high key, "he rid ter the settle*mint* this mornin'; he hev been a-foolin' round thar all day, an' the crap air jes' a-sufferin' fer work! So him an' Uncle Tobe air layin' thar plows in the shop now, kase they air goin' ter run around the corn ter-morrer. Workin', though, goes powerful hard with dad enny time. I tole old Bob Peachin that, when I war ter the mill this evenin'. Him an' the t'other men thar laffed mightily at dad. An' I laffed too!"

There was an angry gleam in Stephen Ryder's stern black

eyes as he turned within, seized the tongs, and thrust a piece
of iron among the coals, while Tobe, who had been asleep in
the window at the back of the shop, rose reluctantly and
plied the bellows. The heavy panting broke forth simulta-
neously with the red flare that quivered out into the dark night.
Presently it faded; the hot iron was whisked upon the anvil,
fiery sparks showered about as the rapid blows fell, and the
echoing crags kept time with rhythmic beats to the clanking
of the sledge and the clinking of the hand-hammer. The
stars, high above the far-stretching mountains, seemed to throb
in unison, until suddenly the blacksmith dealt a sharp blow
on the face of the anvil as a signal to his striker to cease, and
the forge was silent.

As he leaned against the jamb of the door, mechanically ad-
justing his leather apron, he heard Ab's voice again:

"Old Bob say he ain't no 'count sca'cely. He 'lowed ez he
had knowed him many a year, an' f'und him a sneakin', deceivin' critter."

The blacksmith was erect in a moment, every fiber tense.

"That ain't the wust," Ab gabbled on. "Old Bob say,
though 'tain't known ginerally, ez he air gin ter thievin'. Old
Bob 'lowed ter them men, hangin' round the mill, ez he air the
biggest thief on the mounting!"

The strong man trembled. His blood rushed tumultuously
to his head, then seemed to ebb swiftly away. That this should
be said of him to the loafers at the mill! These constituted his
little world. And he valued his character as only an honest
man can. He was amazed at the boldness of the lie. It had
been openly spoken in the presence of his son. One might have
thought the boy would come directly to him. But there he
sat, glibly retailing it to his small comrades! It seemed all
so strange that Stephen Ryder fancied there was surely some

mistake. In the next moment, however, he was convinced that they had been talking of him, and of no one else.

"I tole old Bob ez how I thought they oughtn't ter be so hard on him, ez he warn't thar to speak for hisself."

All three boys giggled weakly, as if this were witty.

"But old Bob 'lowed ez ennybody mought know him by his name. An' then he told me that old sayin':

"'Stephen, Stephen, so deceivin',
That old Satan can't believe him!'"

Here Ben Gryce broke in, begging the others to go home, and come to "borry" the hammer next night. Ab agreed to the latter proposition, but still sat on the log and talked. "Old Bob say," he remarked cheerfully, "that when he do git 'em, he shakes 'em—shakes the life out'n 'em!"

This was inexplicable. Stephen Ryder pondered vainly on it for an instant. But the oft-reiterated formula, "Old Bob say," caught his ears, and he was absorbed anew in Ab's discourse.

"Old Bob say ez my mother air one of the best women in this world. But she air so gi'n ter humoring every critter a-nigh her, an' tends ter 'em so much, an' feeds 'em so high an' hearty, ez they jes' gits good fer nothin' in this world. That's how kem she air eat out'n house an' home now. Old Bob say ez how he air the hongriest critter! Say he jes' despise ter see him comin' round of meal-times. Old Bob say ef he hev got enny good lef' in him, my mother will kill it out yit with kindness."

The blacksmith felt, as he turned back into the shop and roused the sleepy-headed striker, that within the hour all the world had changed for him. These coarse taunts were enough to show in what estimation he was held. And he had fancied himself, in countrified phrase, "respected by all," and had been proud of his standing.

So the bellows began to sigh and pant once more, and kept the red light flaring athwart the darkness. The people down in the valley looked up at it, glowing like a star that had slipped out of the sky and lodged somehow on the mountain, and wondered what Stephen Ryder could be about so late at night. When he left the shop there was no sign of the boys who had ornamented the log earlier in the evening. He walked up the road to his house, and found his wife sitting alone in the rickety little porch.

"Hev that thar boy gone ter bed?" he asked.

"Waal," she slowly drawled, in a soft, placid voice, "he kem hyar 'bout haff an hour ago so nigh crazed ter go ter stay all night with Jim an' Benny Gryce, ez I hed ter let him. Old man Gryce rid by hyar in his wagon on his way home from the settle*mint*. So Ab went off with the Gryce boys an' thar gran'dad."

Thus the blacksmith concluded his tools were not liable to be "borrowed" that night. He had a scheme to insure their safety for the future, but in order to avoid his wife's remonstrances on Ab's behalf he told her nothing of it, nor of what he had overheard.

Early the next morning he set out for the mill, intending to confront "old Bob" and demand retraction. The road down the deep, wild ravine was rugged, and he jogged along slowly until at last he came within sight of the crazy, weather-beaten old building tottering precariously on the brink of the impetuous torrent which gashed the mountain-side. Crags towered above it; vines and mosses clung to its walls; it was a dank, cool, shady place, but noisy enough with the turmoil of its primitive machinery, and the loud, hoarse voices of the loungers striving to make themselves heard above the uproar. There were several of these idle mountaineers aimlessly strolling among the bags of corn and wheat that were piled about. Long dusty cobwebs hung from the rafters. Sometimes a rat, powdered white with flour and rendered reckless by high living, raced boldly across the floor. The golden grain poured ceaselessly through the hopper, and leaning against it was the miller, a tall, stoop-shouldered man about forty years of age, with a floury smile lurking in his beard and a twinkle in his good-humored eyes overhung by heavy, mealy eyebrows.

"Waal, Steve," yelled the miller, shambling forward as the blacksmith appeared in the doorway. "Come 'long in. Whar's yer grist?"

"I hev got no grist!" thundered Steve sternly.

"Waal—ye're jes' ez welcome," said the miller, not noticing the rigid lines of the blacksmith's face, accented here and there by cinders, nor the fierceness of the intent dark eyes.

"I reckon I'm powerful welcome!" sneered Stephen Ryder.

The tone attracted "old Bob's" attention. "What ails ye, Steve?" he asked, surprised.

"I'm a deceivin', sneakin' critter—hey," shouted the visitor, shaking his big fist. He had intended to be calm, but his long-repressed fury had found vent at last.

The miller drew back hastily, astonishment and fear mingled in a pallid paste, as it were, with the flour on his face.

The six startled onlookers stood as if petrified.

"Ye say I'm a thief!—a thief!—a thief!"

With the odious word Ryder made a frantic lunge at the miller, who dodged his strong right arm at the moment when his foot struck against a bag of corn lying on the floor and he stumbled. He recovered his equilibrium instantly. But the six bystanders had seized him.

"Hold him hard, folkses!" cried honest Bob Peachin. "Hold hard! I'll tell ye what ails him—though ye mustn't let on ter him. He air teched in the head!"

He winked at them with a confidential intention as he roared this out, forgetting in his excitement that mental infirmity does not impair the sense of hearing. This folly on his part was a salutary thing for Stephen Ryder. It calmed him instantly. He felt that he had need for caution. A fearful vista of possibilities opened before him. He remembered having seen in his childhood a man reputed to be suddenly bereft of reason, but who he believed was entirely sane, bound hand and foot, and every word, every groan, every effort to free himself, accounted the demonstration of a maniac. This fate was imminent for him. They were seven to one. He trembled as he felt their hands pressing upon the swelling muscles of his arms. With an abrupt realization of his great strength, he waited for a momentary relaxation of their clutch, then with a mighty wrench he burst loose from them, flung himself upon his mare, and dashed off at full speed.

He did no work that afternoon, although the corn was "suffering." He sat after dinner smoking his pipe on the porch of his log cabin, while he moodily watched the big shadow of the mountain creeping silently over the wooded valley as the sun got on the down grade. Deep glooms began to lurk among the ravines of the great ridge opposite. The shimmering blue summits in the distance were purpling. A redbird, alert, crested, and with a brilliant eye, perched idly on the vines about the porch, having relinquished for the day the job of teaching a small, stubby imitation of himself to fly. The shocks of wheat in the bare field close by had turned a rich red gold in the lengthening rays before Stephen Ryder realized that night was close at hand.

All at once he heard a discordant noise which he knew that Ab Ryder called "singing," and presently the boy appeared in the distance, his mouth stretched, his tattered hat stuck on the back of his tow head, his bare feet dusty, his homespun cotton trousers rolled up airily about his knees, his single suspender supporting the structure. His father laughed a little at sight of him, rather sardonically it must be confessed, and saying to his wife that he intended to go to the shop for a while, he rose and strolled off down the road.

When supper was over, however, Ab was immensely relieved to see that his father had no idea of continuing his work. Consequently the usual routine was to be expected. Generally, when summoned to the evening meal, the blacksmith hastily plunged his head in the barrel of water used to temper steel, thrust off his leather apron, and went up to the house without more ado. He smoked afterward, and lounged about, enjoying the relaxation after his heavy work. He did not go down to lock the shop until bedtime, when he was shutting up the house, the barn, and the corn-crib for the night. In the interval the shop stood deserted and open, and this fact was the basis of Ab's opportunity. To-night there seemed to be no deviation from this custom. He ascertained that his father was smoking his pipe on the porch. Then he went down the road and sat on the log near the shop to wait for the other boys who were to share the risks and profits of borrowing the hammer.

All was still—so still! He fancied that he could hear the tumult of the torrent far away as it dashed over the rocks. A dog suddenly began to bark in the black, black valley—then ceased. He was vaguely overawed with the "big mountings" for company, and the distant stars. He listened eagerly for the first cracking of brush which told him that the other boys were near at hand. Then all three crept along cautiously among the huge boles of the trees, feeling very mysterious and important. When they reached the rude window, Ab sat for a moment on the sill, peering into the intense blackness within.

"It air dark thar, fer true, Ab," said Jim Gryce, growing faint-hearted. "Let's go back."

"Naw, sir! Naw, sir!" protested Ab resolutely. "I'm on the borry!"

"How kin we find that thar leetle hammer in sech a dark place?" urged Jim.

"Waal," explained Ab, in his high key, "dad air mightily welded ter his cranky notions. An' he always leaves every tool in the same place edzactly every night. Bound fer me!" he continued in shrill exultation as he slapped his lean leg, "I know whar that thar leetle hammer air sot ter roost!"

He jumped down from the window inside the shop, and cut a wiry caper.

"I'm a man o' bone and muscle!" he bragged. "Kin do ennything."

The other boys followed more quietly. But they had only groped a little distance when Jim Gryce set up a sharp yelp of pain.

"Shet yer mouth, ye pop-eyed catamount!" Ab admonished him. "Dad will hear, an'—ah-h-h!" His own words ended in a shriek. "Oh, my!" vociferated the "man of bone and muscle," who was certainly, too, a man of extraordinary lung power. "Oh, my! The ground is hot—hot ez iron! They always tole me that Satan would ketch me—an' oh, my! now he hev done it!"

He joined the "pop-eyed catamount" in a lively dance with

their bare feet on the hot iron bars which were scattered about the ground in every direction. These were heated artistically, so that they might not really scorch the flesh, but would touch the feelings, and perhaps the conscience. As the third boy's scream rent the air, and told that he, too, had encountered a torrid experience, Ab Ryder became suddenly aware that there was some one besides themselves in the shop. He could see nothing; he was only vaguely conscious of an unexpected presence, and he fancied that it was in the corner by the barrel of water.

All at once a gruff voice broke forth. "I'm on the borry!" it remarked with fierce facetiousness. "I want ter borry a boy—no! a man o' bone an' muscle—fer 'bout a minit and a quarter!" A strong arm seized Ab by his collar. He felt himself swept through the air, soused head foremost into the barrel of water, then thrust into a corner, where he was thankful to find there was no more hot iron.

"I want to borry another boy!" said the gruff voice. And the "pop-eyed catamount" was duly ducked.

"'Twould pleasure me some ter borry another!" the voice declared with grim humor. But Ben was the youngest and smallest, and only led into mischief by the others. They never knew that the blacksmith relented when his turn came, and that he got a mere sprinkle in comparison with their total immersion.

Then Stephen Ryder set out for home, followed by a dripping procession. "I'll l'arn ye ter 'borry' my tools 'thout leave!" he vociferated as he went along.

When they had reached the house, he faced round sternly on Ab. "Whyn't ye kem an' tell me ez how the miller say I war a sneakin', deceivin' critter, an'—an'—an' a thief!"

His wife dropped the dish she was washing, and it broke

unheeded upon the hearth. Ab stretched his eyes and mouth in amazement.

"Old Bob Peachin never tole me no sech word sence I been born!" he declared flatly.

"Then what ailed ye ter go an' tell sech a lie ter Gryce's boys las' night jes' down thar outside o' the shop?" Stephen Ryder demanded.

Ab stared at him, evidently bewildered.

"Ye tole 'em," continued the blacksmith, striving to refresh his memory, "ez Bob Peachin say ez how ye mought know I war deceivin' by my bein' named Stephen—an' that I war the hongriest critter—an'——"

"'Twar the t-a-a-a-rrier!" shouted Ab, "the little rat tarrier ez we war a-talkin' 'bout. He hev been named Steve these six year, old Bob say. He gimme the dog, yestiddy, 'kase I 'lowed ez the rats war eatin' us out'n house an' home, an' my mother hed fed up that old cat o' our'n till he won't look at a mice. Old Bob warned me, though, ez Steve, *the tarrier*, air a mighty thief an' deceivin' ginerally. Old Bob say he reckons my mother will spile the dog with feedin' him, an' kill out what little good he hev got lef' in him with kindness. But I tuk him, an' brung him home ennyhow. An' las' night arter we hed got through talkin' 'bout borryin' "—he looked embarrassed—"the leetle hammer, we tuk to talkin' 'bout the tarrier. An' yander he is now, asleep on the chil'ren's bed!"

A long pause ensued.

"M'ria," said the blacksmith meekly to his wife, "hev ye tuk notice how the gyarden truck air a-thrivin'? 'Pears like ter me ez the peas air a-fullin' up consider'ble."

And so the subject changed.

He had it on his conscience, however, to explain the matter

to the miller. For the second time old Bob Peachin, and the men at the mill "laffed mightily at dad." And when Ab had recovered sufficiently from the exhaustion attendant upon borrowing a hammer, he "laffed too."

—"*The Young Mountaineers.*"

Joseph Quinlan Murphy

Casey at the Bat

It looked extremely rocky for the Mudville nine that day;
The score stood four to six, with but an inning left to play.
And so, when Cooney died at first, and Burrows did the same,
A pallor wreathed the features of the patrons of the game.
A straggling few got up to go, leaving there the rest,
With that hope which springs eternal within the human breast;
For they thought if only Casey could get a whack at that,
They'd put up even money with Casey at the bat.

But Flynn preceded Casey, and likewise so did Blake,
And the former was a pudding, and the latter was a fake;
So on that stricken multitude a deathlike silence sat,
For there seemed but little chance of Casey's getting to the
    bat.

But Flynn let drive a single to the wonderment of all,
And the much despised Blakey tore the cover off the ball,
And when the dust had lifted and they saw what had occurred,
There was Blakey safe on second, and Flynn a-hugging third.

Then from the gladdened multitude went up a joyous yell,
It bounded from the mountain-top and rattled in the dell,
It struck upon the hillside, and rebounded on the flat,
For Casey, mighty Casey, was advancing to the bat.

There was ease in Casey's manner as he stepped into his place;
There was pride in Casey's bearing, and a smile on Casey's
    face;
And when, responding to the cheers, he lightly doffed his hat,
No stranger in the crowd could doubt 'twas Casey at the bat.

Ten thousand eyes were on him as he rubbed his hands with
dirt,

Five thousand tongues applauded as he wiped them on his
shirt;

And while the writhing pitcher ground the ball into his hip,

Defiance gleamed from Casey's eye, a sneer curled Casey's lip.

And now the leather-covered sphere came hurtling through the
air,

And Casey stood a-watching it in haughty grandeur there;

Close by the sturdy batsman the ball unheeded sped—

"That hain't my style," said Casey.   "Strike one," the umpire
said.

From the bleachers black with people there rose a sullen roar,

Like the beating of the storm-waves on a stern and distant
shore;

"Kill him! Kill the umpire!" shouted some one from the
stand—

And it's likely they'd have done it had not Casey raised his
hand.

With a smile of Christian charity great Casey's visage shone;

He stilled the rising tumult, and he bade the game go on;

He signaled to the pitcher, and again the spheroid flew,

But Casey still ignored it, and the umpire said, "Strike two."

"Fraud!" yelled the maddened thousands, and the echo answered "Fraud,"

But one scornful look from Casey, and the audience was awed;

They saw his face grow stern and cold; they saw his muscles
strain,

And they knew that Casey would not let that ball go by again.

The sneer is gone from Casey's lips; his teeth are clinched with
hate,

He pounds with cruel violence his bat upon the plate;

Joseph Quinlan Murphy

And now the pitcher holds the ball, and now he lets it go,
And now the air is shattered by the force of Casey's blow.
Oh! somewhere in this favored land the sun is shining bright,
The band is playing somewhere, and somewhere hearts are
　　　light,
And somewhere men are laughing, and somewhere children
　　　shout,
But there is no joy in Mudville—mighty Casey has "Struck
　　　Out."

Eva L. Ogden

The Sea

SHE was rich, and of high degree;
A poor and unknown artist he.
"Paint me," she said, "a view of the sea."

So he painted the sea as it looked the day
That Aphrodite arose from its spray;
And it broke, as she gazed on its face the while,
Into its countless-dimpled smile.
"What a poky, stupid picture!" said she;
"I don't believe he *can* paint the sea!"

Then he painted a raging, tossing sea,
Storming, with fierce and sudden shock,
Wild cries, and writhing tongues of foam,
A towering, mighty fastness-rock.
In its sides, above those leaping crests,
The thronging sea-birds built their nests.
"What a disagreeable daub!" said she;
"Why, it isn't anything like the sea!"

Then he painted a stretch of hot, brown sand,
With a big hotel on either hand,
And a handsome pavilion for the band—
Not a sign of the water to be seen
Except one faint little streak of green.
"What a perfectly exquisite picture!" said she;
"It's the very *image* of the sea!"

—"*The Century Magazine*," December, 1881.

William Pitt Palmer

Smack in School

A DISTRICT school, not far away,
'Mid Berkshire's hills, one winter's day,
Was humming with its wonted noise
Of threescore mingled girls and boys;
Some few upon their tasks intent,
But more on furtive mischief bent.
The while the master's downward look
Was fastened on a copy-book,
When suddenly, behind his back,
Rose sharp and clear a rousing smack!
As 'twere a battery of bliss
Let off in one tremendous kiss!
"What's that?" the startled master cries.
"That, thir," a little imp replies,
"Wath William Willith, if you pleathe;
I thaw him kith Thuthanna Peathe!"
With frown to make a statue thrill,
The master thundered, "Hither, Will!"
Like wretch o'ertaken in his track,
With stolen chattels on his back,
Will hung his head in fear and shame,
And to the awful presence came—
A great, green, bashful simpleton,
The butt of all good-natured fun.
With smile suppressed, and birch upraised,
The thunderer faltered—"I'm amazed

That you, my biggest pupil, should
Be guilty of an act so rude!
Before the whole set school to boot.
What evil genius put you to't?"
"'Twas she herself, sir," sobbed the lad;
"I did not mean to be so bad;
But when Susannah shook her curls,
And whispered, I was 'fraid of girls,
And dursn't kiss a baby's doll,
I couldn't stand it, sir, at all,
But up and kissed her on the spot!
I know—boo-hoo!—I ought to not,
But, somehow, from her looks—boo-hoo!—
I thought she kind o' wished me to!"

Florence E. Pratt

Courting in Kentucky

WHEN Mary Ann Dollinger got the skule daown thar on Injun
    Bay,
I was glad, fer I like ter see a gal makin' her honest way.
I heerd some talk in the village abaout her flyin' high,
Tew high fer busy farmer folks with chores ter do ter fly;
But I paid no sorter attention ter all the talk ontell
She come in her reg'lar boardin' raound ter visit with us a
    spell.
My Jake an' her had been cronies ever since they could walk
An' it tuk me aback to hear her kerrectin' him in his talk.

Jake ain't no hand at grammar, though he hain't his beat for
    work;
But I sez ter myself, "Look out, my gal, yer a-foolin' with a
    Turk!"
Jake bore it wonderful patient, an' said in a mournful way,
He p'sumed he was behindhand with the doin's at Injun Bay.
I remember once he was askin' for some o' my Injun buns,
An' she said he should allus say "them air," stid o' "them is"
    the ones.
Wal, Mary Ann kep' at him stiddy mornin' an' evenin' long,
Tell he dassent open his mouth for fear o' talkin' wrong.

One day I was pickin' currants daown by the old quince-tree,
When I heerd Jake's voice a-sayin', "Be yer willin' ter marry
    me?"

An' Mary Ann kerrectin', " 'Air ye willin',' yeou sh'd say;"
Our Jake he put his foot daown in a plum decided way,
"No wimmen-folks is a-goin' ter be rearrangin' me.
Hereafter I says 'craps,' 'them is,' 'I calk'late,' an' 'I be.'
Ef folks don't like my talk, they needn't hark ter what I say;
But I ain't a-goin' to take no sass from folks from Injun Bay.
I asked you free an' final, 'Be ye goin' ter marry me?'"
An' Mary Ann says, tremblin', yet anxious-like, "I be."

Frances Lee Pratt

Captain Ben's Choice

AN old red house on a rocky shore, with a fisherman's blue
boat rocking on the bay, and two white sails glistening far away
over the water. Above, the blue, shining sky; and below,
the blue, shining sea.

"It seems clever to have a pleasant day," said Mrs. Davids,
sighing.

Mrs. Davids said everything with a sigh, and now she wiped
her eyes also on her calico apron. She was a woman with
a complexion like faded seaweed, who seemed always pitying
herself.

"I tell them," said she, "I have had real hard luck. My
husband is buried off in California, and my son died in the
army and is buried down South. Neither one of them is buried
together."

Then she sighed again. Twice, this time.

"And so," she continued, taking out a pinch of bayberry
snuff, "I am left alone in the world. *Alone*, I say! Why,
I've got a daughter, but she is away out West. She is married
to an engineer-man. And I've got two grandchildren."

Mrs. Davids took the pinch of bayberry and shook her head,
looking as though that was the "hardest luck" of all.

"Well, everybody has to have their pesters, and you'll have
to take yours," rejoined Miss Persis Tame, taking a pinch of
snuff—the real maccaboy—twice as large, with twice as fierce
an action. "I don't know what it is to bury children, nor to
lose a husband; I s'pose I don't; but I know what it is to be
jammed round the world and not have a ruff to stick my head

193

under. I wish I had all the money I ever spent traveling—and *that's* twelve dollars," she continued regretfully.

"Why in the world don't you marry and have a home of your own?" sighed Mrs. Davids.

"Well, I don't *expect* to marry. I don't know as I do, at my time of life," responded the spinster. "I rather guess my day for chances is gone by."

"You ain't such a dreadful sight older than I am, though," replied Mrs. Davids reflectively.

"Not so old by two full years," returned Miss Tame, taking another smart pinch of snuff, as though it touched the empty spot in her heart and did it good. "But *you* ain't looking out for opportunities yet, I suppose."

Mrs. Davids sighed evasively. "We can't tell what is before us. There is more than one man in want of a wife."

As though to point her words, Captain Ben Lundy came in sight on the beach, his head a long way forward, and his shambling feet trying in vain to keep up.

"Thirteen months and a half since Lyddy was buried," continued Mrs. Davids, accepting this application to her words, "and there is Captain Ben taking up with just what housekeeper he can get, and *no* housekeeper at all. It would be an excellent home for you, Persis. Captain Ben always had the name of making a kind husband."

She sighed again, whether from regret for the bereaved man or for the multitude of women bereft of such a husband.

By this time Captain Ben's head was at the door.

"Morning!" said he, while his feet were coming up. "Quite an accident down here below the lighthouse last night. Schooner ran ashore in the blow and broke all up into kindling-wood in less than no time. Captain Tisdale's been out looking for dead bodies ever since daylight."

"I knowed it," sighed Mrs. Davids. "I heard a rushing sound some time about the break of day that waked me out of a sound sleep, and I knowed then there was a spirit leaving its body. I heard it the night Davids went, or I expect I did. It must have been very nearly at that time."

"Well, I guess it wasn't a spirit last night," said Captain Ben; "for, as I was going on to say, after searching back and forth, Captain Tisdale came upon the folks, a man and a boy, rolled up in their wet blankets asleep behind the lifeboat house. He said he felt like he could shake them for staying out in the wet. Wrecks always make for the lighthouse, so he s'posed those ones were drowned to death, sure enough."

"Oh, then it couldn't have been them I was warned of!" returned Mrs. Davids, looking as though she regretted it. "It was right over my head, and I waked up just as the thing was rushing past. You haven't heard, have you," she continued, "whether or no there was any other damage done by the gale?"

"I don't know whether you would call it damage exactly," returned Captain Ben, "but Loizah Mullers got so scared she left me and went home. She said she couldn't stay and run the chance of another of our coast blows, and off she trapsed."

Mrs. Davids sighed like November. "So you have some hard luck as well as myself. I don't suppose you can *get* a housekeeper to keep her long," said she dismally.

"Abel Grimes tells me it is enough sight easier getting wives than housekeepers, and I'm some of a mind to try that tack," replied Captain Ben, smiling grimly.

Mrs. Davids put up her hand to feel of her hair, and smoothed down her apron; while Miss Persis Tame blushed like a withered rose and turned her eyes modestly out of the window.

"I am *so*. But the difficulty is, who will it be? There are so many to select from, it is fairly bothersome," continued Captain Ben, winking fast and looking as though he was made of dry corn-cobs and hay.

Miss Persis Tame turned about abruptly. "The land alive!" she ejaculated with such sudden emphasis that the dishes shook on their shelves and Captain Ben in his chair. "It makes me mad as a March hare to hear men go on as though all they'd got to do was to throw down their handkerchers to a woman, and, no matter who, she'd spring and run to pick it up. It is always 'Who will I marry?' and not 'Who will marry me?'"

"Why, there is twice the number of widders that there is of widderers here at the P'int. That was what was in my mind," said Captain Ben, in a tone of meek apology. "There is the Widow Keens, she that was Azubah Muchmore. I don't know but what she would do. Lyddy used to think everything of her, and she is a first rate of a housekeeper."

"Perhaps so," assented Mrs. Davids dubiously. "But she is troubled a sight with the head complaint. I suppose you know she is. That is against her."

"Yes," assented Miss Tame. "The Muchmores all have weak heads. And, too, the Widow Keens, she's had a fall lately. She was up in a chair cleaning her top buttery shelf, and somehow one of the chair legs give way—it was loose, or something, I expect—and down she went her whole heft. She keeps about, but she goes with two staves."

"I want to know if that is so," said Captain Ben, his honest soul warming with sudden sympathy. "The widder has seen a sight of trouble."

"Yes, she has lived through a good deal, that woman has. I couldn't live through so much, 'pears to me. But we don't know what we can live through," rejoined Miss Tame.

Captain Ben did not reply, but his ready feet began to move to and fro restlessly; for his heart, more ready yet, had already gone out toward the unfortunate widow.

"It is so bad for a woman to be alone," said he to himself, shambling along the shingly beach a moment after. "Nobody to mend her chairs or split up her kindlings, or do a chore for her; and she lame into the bargain. It is *too* bad."

"He has steered straight for the Widow Keens's as sure as A is apple-dumpling," remarked Miss Persis, peering after him from the window.

"Well, I must admit I wouldn't have thought of Captain Ben's being en-a-mored after such a sickly piece of business. But men never know what they want. Won't you just hand me that gum-cam-phyer bottle, now you are up? It is on that chest of drawers behind you."

"No more they don't," returned Miss Tame, with a plaintive cadence, taking a sniff from the camphor bottle on the way. "However, I don't begrutch him to her—I don't know as I do. It will make her a good hum, though, if she concludes to make arrangements."

Meantime, Captain Ben Lundy's head was well-nigh to Mrs. Keens's door, for it was situated only around the first sand-hill. She lived in a little bit of a house that looked as though it had been knocked together for a crockery-crate, in the first place, with two windows and a rude door thrown in as afterthoughts. In the rear of this house was another tiny building something like a grown-up hen-coop; and this was where Mrs. Keens carried on the business bequeathed to her by her deceased husband, along with five small children and one not so small, but, worse than that, one who was "not altogether there," as the English say.

She was about this business now, dressed in a primitive

sort of bloomer, with a wash-tub and clothes-wringer before her, and an army of bathing-suits of every kind and color flapping wildly in the fresh sea air at one side.

From a little farther on, mingling with the sound of the beating surf, came the merry voices of bathers—boarders at the great hotels on the hill.

"Here you be! Hard at it!" said Captain Ben, puffing around the corner like a portable west wind. "I've understood you've had a hurt. Is that so?"

"Oh, no! Nothing to mention," returned Mrs. Keens, turning about a face bright and cheerful as the full moon; and throwing, as by accident, a red bathing-suit, over the two broomsticks that leaned against her tub.

Unlike Mrs. Davids, Mrs. Keens neither pitied herself nor would allow anybody else to do so.

"Sho!" remarked Captain Ben, feeling defrauded. He had counted on sacrificing himself to his sympathies, but he didn't give up yet. "You must see some pretty tough times, 'pears to me, with such a parcel of little ones, and only yourself to look to," said he, proceeding awkwardly enough to hang the pile of wrung-out clothes upon an empty line.

"I don't complain," returned the widow bravely. "My children are not *teusome;* and Jack, why, you would be surprised to see how many things Jack can do, for all he isn't quite right."

As she spoke thus with affectionate pride, Jack came up from the beach wheeling a roughly made cart filled with wet bathing-clothes. He looked up at sound of his mother's voice with something of the dumb tenderness of an intelligent dog. "Jack helps; Jack good boy," said he, nodding with a happy smile.

"Yes, Jack helps. We don't complain," repeated the mother.

"It would come handy, though, to have a man around to see to things and kind o' provide, wouldn't it, though?" persisted Captain Ben.

"Some might think so," replied Mrs. Keens, stopping her wringer to reflect a little. "But I haven't any wish to change my situation," she added decidedly, going on again with her work.

"Sure on't?" persisted the captain.

"Certain," replied the widow.

Captain Ben sighed. "I thought maybe you was having a hard row to hoe, and I thought like enough——"

What he never said, excepting by a beseeching glance at the cheerful widow, for just then an interruption came from some people after bathing-suits.

So Captain Ben moved off with a dismal countenance. But before he had gone far it suddenly brightened. "It might not be for the best," quoth he to himself. "Like enough not. I was very careful not to commit myself, and I am very glad I didn't." He smiled as he reflected on his judicious wariness. "But, however," he continued, "I might as well finish up this business now. There is Rachel Doolittle. Who knows but she'd make a likely wife? Lyddy sot a good deal by her. She never had a quilting or a sewing bee but what nothing would do but she must give Rachel Doolittle an invite. Yes; I wonder I never decided on her before. She will be glad of a home, sure enough, for she haves to live around, as it were, upon her brothers."

Captain Ben's feet quickened themselves at these thoughts, and had almost overtaken his head, when behold! at a sudden turn in the road there stood Miss Rachel Doolittle, picking barberries from a wayside bush. "My sakes! If she ain't right here, like Rachel in the Bible!" ejaculated Captain Ben, taking heart at the omen.

Miss Doolittle looked up from under her tied-down brown hat in surprise at such a salutation. But her surprise was increased by Captain Ben's next remark.

"It just came into my mind," said he, "that you was the right one to take Lyddy's place. You two used to be such great knit-ups, that it will seem 'most like having Lyddy back again. No," he continued, after a little reflection, "I don't know of anybody I had rather see sitting in Lyddy's chair and wearing Lyddy's things than yourself."

"Dear me, Captain Lundy, I couldn't think of it. Paul's folks expect me to stay with them while the boarder season lasts, and I've as good as promised Jacob's wife I'll spend the winter with her."

"Ain't that a hard life you are laying out for yourself? And then bum-by you will get old or sick maybe, and who is going to want you around then? Every woman needs a husband of her own to take care of her."

"I'm able to take care of myself as yet, thanks to goodness! And I am not afraid my brothers will see me suffer in case of sickness," returned Miss Doolittle, her cheeks flaming up like a sumach in October.

"But hadn't you better take a little time to think it over? Maybe it come sudden to you," pleaded Captain Ben.

"No, I thank you. Some things don't need thinking over," answered Miss Doolittle, plucking at the barberries more diligently than ever.

"I wish Lyddy was here. She would convince you you were standing in your own light," returned Lyddy's widower in a perplexed tone.

"I don't need one to come from the dead to show me my own mind," retorted Miss Doolittle firmly.

"Well, like enough you are right," said Captain Ben mildly, putting a few stems of barberries in her pail; "maybe it wouldn't be best. I don't want to be rash." And with that he moved off, on the whole congratulating himself he had not decided to marry Miss Doolittle.

"I thought, after she commenced her miserable gift of the gab, that Lyddy used to be free to admit she had a fiery tongue, for all they were such friends. And I'm all for peace myself. I guess, on the whole, maybe she ain't the one for me, perhaps, and it is as well to look further. *Why!* What in *the* world! Well, there! what have I been thinking of? There is Mrs. Davids, as neat as a new cent, and the master hand to save. She is always taking on; and she will be glad enough to have somebody to look out for her. Why, sure enough! And there I was right at her house this very day, and never once thought of her! What an old dunce!"

But, fortunately, this not being a sin of *com*mission, it could be rectified; and directly Captain Ben had turned about and was trotting again toward the red house on the beach.

"Pound for pound of the best white sugar," he heard Miss Tame say as he neared the door.

"White sugar!" repeated Mrs. Davids, her usual sigh drawn out into a little groan. "*White* sugar for *cram*berries! Who ever heard of such a thing? I've always considered I did well when I had plenty of brown."

"Poor creeter!" thought Captain Ben. "How she would enjoy getting into my pantry! Lyddy never complained that she didn't have enough of everything to do *with*."

And in the full ardor of his intended benevolence, he went right in and opened the subject at once. But, to his astonishment, Mrs. Davids refused him. She sighed, but she refused him.

"I've seen trouble enough a'ready, without my rushing into more with my eyes wide open," sighed she.

"Trouble? Why, that is just what I was meaning to save you!" exclaimed the bewildered widower. "Pump right in the house, and stove e'enamost new. And Lyddy never knew what it was to want for a spoonful of sugar or a pound of flour. And such a *handy* buttery and sink! Lyddy used to say she felt the worst about leaving her buttery of anything."

"Should thought she would," answered Mrs. Davids, forgetting to sigh. "However, I can't say that I feel any hankering after marrying a buttery. I've got buttery-room enough here, without the trouble of getting set up in a new place."

"Just as you say," returned the rejected. "I ain't sure as you'd be exactly the one. I *was* a-thinking of looking for somebody a little younger."

"Well, here is Persis Tame. Why don't you bespeak her? *She* is younger, and she is in need of a good home. I can recommend her, too, as the first rate of a cook," remarked Mrs. Davids benevolently.

Miss Tame had been sitting a little apart by the open window smiling to herself.

But now she turned about at once. "H'm!" said she, with contempt; "I should rather live under an umbrella tied to a stake than marry for a *hum*."

So Captain Ben went home without engaging either wife or housekeeper.

And the first thing he saw was Captain Jacob Doolittle's old one-eyed horse eating the apples Loizah Mullers had strung and festooned from nails against the house to dry.

The next thing he saw was that, having left a window open, the hens had flown in and gone to housekeeping on their own account. But they were not, like Mrs. Davids, as neat as a new cent, and *not*, also, such master hands to save.

"Shoo! Shoo! Get out! Go 'long there with you!" cried Captain Ben, waving the dish-cloth and the poker. "I declare for't! I most hadn't ought to have left that bread out on the table. They've made a pretty mess of it, and it is every speck there is in the house too. Well, I must make a do of potatoes for supper, with a bit of pie and a mouthful of cake."

Accordingly he went to work building a fire that wouldn't burn. Then, forgetting the simple matter of dampers, the potatoes wouldn't bake. The tea-kettle boiled over and cracked the stove, and, after that, boiled dry and cracked itself. Finally the potatoes fell to baking with so much ardor that they overdid it and burned up. And, last of all, the cake-jar and pie-cupboard proved to be entirely empty. Loizah had left on the eve of baking-day.

"The old cat! Well, I'd just as soon live on slapjacks a spell," said Captain Ben, when he made this discovery.

But even slapjacks palled on his palate, especially when he had them always to cook for himself.

"'Tain't no way to live, this ain't," said he at last. "I'm a good mind to marry as ever I had to eat."

So he put on his hat and walked out. The first person he met was Miss Persis Tame, who turned her back and fell to picking thoroughwort blossoms as he came up.

"Look a-here," said he, stopping short, "I'm dreadful put to't. I can't get ne'er a wife nor ne'er a housekeeper, and I am e'enamost starved to death. I wish you *would* consent to marry with me, if you feel as if you could bring your mind to it. I am sure it would have been Lyddy's wish."

Miss Tame smelt of the thoroughwort blossoms.

"It comes pretty sudden on me," she replied. "I hadn't

given the subject any thought. But you *are* to be pitied in your situation."

"Yes. And I'm dreadful lonesome. I've always been used to having Lyddy to talk over things with, and I miss her a sight. And I don't know anybody that has her ways more than you have. You are a good deal such a built woman, and you have the same hitch to your shoulders when you walk. You've got something the same look to your eyes too; I noticed it last Sunday in meeting-time," continued the widower anxiously.

"I do feel for you. A man alone is in a deplorable situation," replied Miss Tame. "I'm sure I'd do anything in my power to help you."

"Well, marry with me, then. That is what I want. We could be real comfortable together. I'll go for the license this minute, and we'll be married right away," returned the impatient suitor. "You go up to Elder Crane's, and I'll meet you there as soon as I can fetch around."

Then he hurried away, "without giving me a chance to say 'No,'" said "she that was" Persis Tame, afterward. "So I *had* to marry with him, as you might say. But I've never seen cause to regret it. I've got a first rate of a hum, and Captain Ben makes a first rate of a husband. And no hain't he, I hope, found cause to regret it," she added, with a touch of wifely pride; "though I do expect he might have had his pick among all the single women at the Point; but out of them all he chose *me*."

Albert Riddle

A Poem of Every-Day Life

HE tore him from the merry throng
    Within the billiard hall;
He was gotten up regardlessly
    To pay his party call.
His thoughts were dire and dark within,
    Discourteous to fate:
"Ah, me! these social debts incurred
    Are hard to liquidate."

His boots were slender, long, and trim;
    His collar tall and swell;
His hats were made by Dunlap,
    And his coats were cut by Bell;
A symphony in black and white,
    "Of our set" the pride,
Yet he lingered on his way—
    He would that he had died.

His feet caressed the lonely way,
    The pave gave forth no sound;
They seemed in pitying silence clothed—
    West End-ward he was bound.
He approached the mansion stealthily,
    The step looked cold and chill;
He glanced into the vestibule,
    But all was calm and still.

He fingered nervously the bell,
    His card-case in his hand;
He saw the mirror in the hall—
    Solemn, stately, grand.

Suddenly his spirits rose;
  The drawing-room looked dim;
The menial filled his soul with joy
  With "No, there's no one in."

With fiendish glee he stole away;
  His heart was gay and light,
Happy that he went and paid
  His party call that night.
His steps turned to the billiard hall,
  Blissfully he trod;
He entered: "What, returned so soon?"
  Replied: "She's out, thank God!"

Sixteen cues were put to rest
  Within their upright beds,
And sixteen different tiles were placed
  On sixteen level heads;
Sixteen men upon the street
  In solid phalanx all,
And sixteen men on duty bent
  To pay *their* party call.

When the fairest of her sex came home
  At early dawn, I ween,
She slowly looked the cards all out—
  They numbered seventeen.
With calm relief she raised her eyes,
  Filled with grateful light,
"Oh, merciful Fate, look down and see
  What I've escaped this night!"

James Gardner Sanderson

The Conundrum of the Golf-Links

(With thanks to Kipling)

WHEN the flush of the new-born sun fell first on Eden's gold
    and green,
Our Father Adam sat under the Tree and shaved his driver
    clean,
And joyously whirled it round his head and knocked the
    apples off,
Till the devil whispered behind the leaves, "Well done—but
    is it golf?"

Wherefore he called his wife, and fled to practise again his
    swing—
The first of the world who foozled his stroke (yet the grand-
    papa of Tyng);
And he left his clubs to the use of his sons—and that was a
    glorious gain,
When the devil chuckled "Beastly Golf" in the ear of the
    horrored Cain.

They putted and drove in the North and South; they talked
    and laid links in the West;
Till the waters rose o'er Ararat's tees, and the aching wrists
    could rest—
Could rest till that blank, blank canvasback heard the devil
    jeer and scoff,
As he flew with the flood-fed olive branch, "Dry weather.
    Let's play golf."

They pulled and sliced and pounded the earth, and the balls
    went sailing off
Into bunkers and trees, while the devil grinned "Keep your
    eye on it! *That's* not golf."
Then the devil took his sulphured cleek and mightily he swung,
While each man marveled and cursed his form, and each in an
    alien tongue.

The tale is as old as the Eden tree, and new as the newest
    green,
For each man knows ere his lip thatch grows the caddy's
    mocking mien.
And each man hears, though the ball falls fair, the devil's
    cursed cough
Of joy as the man holes out in ten, "You did it—but what
    poor golf!"

We have learned to whittle the Eden tree to the shape of a
    niblick's shaft;
We have learned to make a mashie with a wondrous handi-
    craft;
We know that a hazard is often played best by redriving off,
But the devil whoops as he whooped of old, "It's easy, but is
    it golf?"

When the flicker of summer falls faint on the club room's
    gold and green,
The sons of Adam sit them down and boast of strokes unseen;
They talk of stymies and brassie lies to the tune of the steward's
    cough,
But the devil whispers in their ears, "Gadzooks! but that's
    not golf."

James Gardner Sanderson

Now if we could win to the Eden tree where the Nine-Mile
    Links are laid,
And seat ourselves where man first swore as he drove from the
    grateful shade,
And if we could play where our fathers played, and follow our
    swings well through,
By the favor of God we might know of golf what our Father
    Adam knew.

Harrison Robertson

Kentucky Philosophy

"You Wi'yum, cum 'ere, suh, dis minnit! Wut dat you got
  under dat box?
I don't want no foolin'—you hear me? Wut you say? Ain't
  nu'h'n but *rocks?*
'Peahs ter me you's owdashus perticler. S'posin' dey's uv a
  new kine.
I'll des take a look at dem rocks. Hi yi! der you t'ink dat I's
  bline?

"I calls dat a plain watermillion, you scamp, en I knows
  whah it growed;
It come fum de Jimmerson cawn-fiel', dah on ter side er de
  road.
You stole it, you rascal—you stole it! I watched you fum
  down in de lot.
En time I gits th'ough wid you, nigger, you won't eb'n be a
  grease spot!

"I'll fix you—Mirandy! Mirandy! Go cut me a hick'ry—
  make has'e!
En cut me de toughes' en keenes' you c'n fine anywhah on de
  place—
I'll larn you, Mr. Wi'yum Joe Vetters, ter steal en ter lie, you
  young sinner,
Disgracin' yo' ole Christian mammy, en makin' her leave
  cookin' dinner!

Harrison Robertson

"Now ain't you ashamed er yo'se'f, suh? I is. I's 'shamed
    you's my son!
En de holy accorjun angel he's 'shamed er wut you has done;
En he's tuk it down up yander in coal-black blood-red letters—
'One watermillion stoled by Wi'yum Josephus Vetters.'

"En wut you s'posin' Brer Bascom, yo' teacher at Sunday-
    school,
'Ud say ef he knowed how you's broke de good Lawd's Gol'n
    Rule?
Boy, whah's de raisin' I give you? Is you boun' fuh ter be a
    black villiun?
I's s'prised dat a chile er yo' mammy 'ud steal any man's
    watermillion.

"En I's now gwiner cut it right open, en you shain't have
    narry bite,
Fuh a boy who'll steal watermillion—en dat in de day's broad
    light—
Ain't— *Lawdy!* it's GREEN! Mirandy! Mi-ran-dy! come on
    wi' dat switch!
Well, stealin' a g-r-e-e-n watermillion! Who ever heered tell
    er des sich?

"'Cain't tell w'en dey's ripe?' W'y you thump 'um, en w'en
    dey go 'pank,' dey is green;
But when dey go '*punk*'—now you mine me—dey's ripe,
    en dat's des wut I mean.
En nex' time you hook watermillions—*you* heered me, you
    ign'ant young hunk,
Ef you don't want a lickin' all over, be sho' dat dey allers go
    'punk!'"

Frederick William Shelton

Incidents in a Retired Life

Last year I had a solitary peach upon a solitary tree, for the early frost frustrated the delicious crop. This only one, which, from its golden color, might be entitled El Dorado, I watched with fear and trembling from day to day, patiently waiting for the identical time when I should buoy it up carefully in my hand, that its pulp should not be bruised, tear off its thin peel, admonished that the time had come by a gradual releasing of the fruit from its adhesion to the stem, and I appointed the next day for the ceremonial of plucking. The morrow dawned, as bright a day as ever dawned upon the earth, and on a near approach I found it still there, and said, with chuckling gratification, "There is some delicacy in thieves." Alas! on reaching it, somebody had taken a large bite out of the ripest cheek, but with a sacrilegious witticism had left it sticking to the stem. The detestable prints of the teeth which bit it were still in it, and a wasp was gloating at its core. Had he taken the whole peach I should have vented my feelings in a violence of indignation unsuited to a balmy garden. But as he was joker enough to bite only its sunny side, I must forgive him, as one who has some element of salvation in his character, because he is disposed to look at the bright side of things. What is a peach? A mere globe of succulent and delicious pulp, which I would rather be deprived of than cultivate bad feelings, even toward thieves. Wherever you find rogues whose deeds involve a saline element of wit, make up your mind that they are no rogues.—"*Up the River.*"

Frederick William Shelton

THIS morning the Shanghai hen laid another egg, of a rich brunette complexion, which we took away, and replaced by a common vulgar egg, intending to reserve the Shanghai's in a cool place until the time of incubation. Very much amused was I with the sequel. The proud and haughty superiority of the breed manifested itself by detecting the cheat and resenting the insult. Shang and Eng flew at the supposititious egg with the utmost indignation and picked it to pieces, scratching the remnants of the shell from the nest. . . . There is one peculiarity of these fowls which deserves to be mentioned. When I removed mine from the basket I thought that the worthy donor had clipped their wings to prevent them from flying away or scaling the hennery. On further knowledge I have learned that their style and fashion is that of the jacket-sleeve and bobtail coat. Their eminent domesticity is clearly signified by this, because they cannot get over an ordinary fence, and would not if they could. It is because they have no disposition to do this, that Nature has cropped them of their superfluous wings and given them a plumage suitable to their desires. "Their sober wishes never learn to stray." They often come into the kitchen, but never go abroad to associate with common fowls, but remain at home in dignified retirement. Another thing remarkable and quite renowned about this is the Oriental courtesy and politeness of the cock. If you throw a piece of bread, he waits till the hen helps herself first, and often carries it to her in his own beak. The feathered people in the East, and those *not* feathered, are far superior to ours in those elaborate and delightful forms of manner which add a charm and zest to life. This has been from the days of Abraham until now. There are no common people in these realms. All are polite, and the very roosters illustrate the best principles laid down in any book of etiquette. *Book of Etiquette!* What is conventionalism without the inborn sense? Can any man or beast be taught to be mechanically polite? Not at all—not at all! . . .

I have received a present of a pair of Cochin-Chinas, a superb cock and a dun-colored hen. I put them with my other fowls in the cellar, to protect them for a short time from the severity of the weather. My Shanghai rooster had for several nights been housed up; for on one occasion, when the cold was snapping, he was discovered under the lee of a stone wall, standing on one leg, taking no notice of the approach of any one, and nearly gone. When brought in, he backed up against the red-hot kitchen stove, and burned his tail off. Before this he had no feathers in the rear to speak of, and now he is bobtailed indeed. Anne sewed upon him a jacket of carpet, and put him in a tea-box for the night; and it was ludicrous on the next morning to see him lifting up his head above the square prison-box and crowing lustily to greet the day. But before breakfast-time he had a dreadful fit. He retreated against the wall, he fell upon his side, he kicked, and he "carried on"; but when the carpet was taken off he came to himself, and ate corn with a voracious appetite. His indisposition was, no doubt, occasioned by a rush of blood to the head from the tightness of the bandages. When Shanghai and Cochin met together in the cellar, they enacted in that dusky hole all the barbarities of a profane cockpit. I heard a sound as if from the tumbling of barrels, followed by a dull, thumping noise, like spirit-rappings, and went below, where the first object which met my eye was a mouse creeping along the beam out of an excavation in my pineapple cheese. As for the fowls, instead of salutation after the respectful manner of their country—which is expressed thus: Shang knocks knees to Cochin, bows three times, touches the ground, and makes obeisance—they were engaged in a bloody fight, unworthy of Celestial poultry. With their heads down, eyes flashing, and red as vipers, and with a feathery frill or ruffle about their necks, they were leaping at each other, to see who should hold dominion over the ash-heap. It put me exactly in mind of two Scythians or two Greeks in America, where each wished to be considered the only Scythian or only Greek in the country. A contest or emulation is at all times highly animating and full of zest, whether two scholars write, two athletes strive, two boilers strain, or two cocks fight. Every lazy dog in the vicinity is immediately at hand. I looked on until I saw the Shanghai's peepers darkened and his comb streaming with blood. These birds contended for some days after for preeminence on the lawn, and no flinching could be observed on either part, although the Shanghai was by one-third the smaller of the two. At last the latter was thoroughly mortified; his eyes wavered and wandered vaguely, as he stood opposite the foe; he turned tail and ran. From that moment he became the veriest coward, and submitted to every indignity without attempting to resist. He suffered himself to be chased about the lawn, fled from the Indian meal, and was almost starved. Such submission on his part at last resulted in peace, and the two rivals walked side by side without fighting, and ate together, with a mutual concession, of the corn. This, in turn, engendered a degree of presumption on the part of the Shanghai cock; and one day, when the dew sparkled and the sun shone peculiarly bright, he so far forgot himself as to ascend a hillock and venture on a tolerably triumphant crow. It showed a lack of judgment; his cock-a-doodle-doo proved fatal. Scarcely had he done so, when Cochin-China rushed upon him, tore out his feathers, and flogged him so severely that it was doubtful whether he would remain with us. Now, alas! he presents a sad spectacle; his comb frozen off, his tail burned off, and his head knocked to a jelly. While the corn jingles in the throats of his compeers when they eagerly snap it, as if they were eating from a pile of shilling pieces or fi'penny bits, he stands aloof and grubs in the ground. How changed!

—"*Up the River.*"

Joseph Bert Smiley

St. Peter at the Gate

ST. PETER stood guard at the golden gate,
With a solemn mien and an air sedate,
When up to the top of the golden stair
A man and a woman, ascending there,
Applied for admission. They came and stood
Before St. Peter, so great and good,
In hopes the City of Peace to win,
And asked St. Peter to let them in.
The woman was tall, and lank, and thin,
With a scraggy beadlet upon her chin;
The man was short, and thick, and stout;
His stomach was built so it rounded out;
His face was pleasant, and all the while
He wore a kindly and genial smile.
The choirs in the distance the echoes woke,
And the man kept still while the woman spoke:
"Oh, thou who guardest the gate," said she,
"We two come hither beseeching thee
To let us enter the heavenly land,
And play our harps with the angel band.
Of me, St. Peter, there is no doubt—
There is nothing from heaven to bar me out;
I have been to meetings three times a week,
And almost always I'd rise and speak.
I've told the sinners about the day
When they'd repent their evil way;

217

I have told my neighbors, I have told them all,
'Bout Adam and Eve, and the primal fall;
I've shown them what they'd have to do
If they'd pass in with the chosen few;
I've marked their path of duty clear—
Laid out the plan for their whole career;
I've talked and talked to 'em, loud and long,
For my lungs are good and my voice is strong.
So, good St. Peter, you'll clearly see
The gate of heaven is open to me.
But my old man, I regret to say,
Hasn't walked exactly the narrow way;
He smokes and he swears, and grave faults he's got,
And I don't know whether he will pass or not.
He never would pray with an earnest vim,
Or go to revival, or join in a hymn;
So I had to leave him in sorrow there,
While I, with the chosen, united in prayer.
He ate what the pantry chanced to afford,
While I, in my purity, sang to the Lord;
And if cucumbers were all he got,
It's a chance if he merited them or not.
But oh, St. Peter, I love him so!
To the pleasures of heaven please let him go!
I've done enough—a saint I've been.
Won't that atone? Can't you let him in?
By my grim gospel I know 'tis so,
That the unrepentant must fry below;
But isn't there some way that you can see,
That he may enter who's dear to me?
It's a narrow gospel by which I pray,
But the chosen expect to find some way

Joseph Bert Smiley

Of coaxing, or fooling, or bribing you,
So that their relation can amble through.
And say, St. Peter, it seems to me
This gate isn't kept as it ought to be.
You ought to stand by that opening there,
And never sit down in that easy chair.
And say, St. Peter, my sight is dimmed,
But I don't like the way your whiskers are trimmed;
They're cut too wide, and outward toss:
They'd look better narrower, cut straight across.
Well, we must be going our crowns to win,
So open, St. Peter, and we'll pass in."
St. Peter sat quiet and stroked his staff,
But spite of his office he had to laugh;
Then said, with a fiery gleam in his eye,
"Who's tending this gateway—you, or I?"
And then he arose in his stature tall,
And pressed a button upon the wall,
And said to the imp who answered the bell,
"Escort this lady around to hell!"
The man stood still as a piece of stone—
Stood sadly, gloomily there alone;
A lifelong, settled idea he had
That his wife was good and he was bad.
He thought, if the woman went down below,
That he would certainly have to go;
That if she went to the regions dim,
There wasn't a ghost of a show for him.
Slowly he turned, by habit bent,
To follow wherever the woman went.
St. Peter, standing on duty there,
Observed that the top of his head was bare.

He called the gentleman back, and said,
"Friend, how long have you been wed?"
"Thirty years" (with a weary sigh),
And then he thoughtfully added, "Why?"
St. Peter was silent. With head bent down,
He raised his hand and scratched his crown;
Then, seeming a different thought to take,
Slowly, half to himself, he spake:
"Thirty years with that woman there?
No wonder the man hasn't any hair!
Swearing is wicked, smoke's not good.
He smoked and swore—I should think he would.
Thirty years with that tongue so sharp!
Ho, Angel Gabriel! give him a harp—
A jeweled harp with a golden string.
Good sir, pass in where the angels sing.
Gabriel, give him a seat alone—
One with a cushion, up near the throne;
Call up some angels to play their best;
Let him enjoy the music in rest;
See that on finest ambrosia he feeds;
He's had about all the hell he needs.
It isn't just hardly the thing to do,
To roast him on earth, and the future too."
They gave him a harp with golden strings,
A glittering robe, with a pair of wings,
And he said, as he entered the Realm of Day,
"Well, this beats cucumber, anyway!"
And so the Scriptures had come to pass
"The last shall be first, and the first shall be last."

Sol Smith

A Bully Boat and a Brag Captain

A Story of Steamboat Life on the Mississippi

DOES any one remember the *Caravan?* She was what would now be considered a slow boat; then (1827) she was regularly advertised as the "fast-running," etc. Her regular trips from New Orleans to Natchez were usually made in from six to eight days; a trip made by her in five days was considered remarkable. A voyage from New Orleans to Vicksburg and back, including stoppages, generally entitled the officers and crew to a month's wages. Whether the *Caravan* ever achieved the feat of a voyage to the Falls (Louisville) I have never learned. If she did, she must have "had a *time* of it!"

It was my fate to take passage in this boat. The captain was a good-natured, easy-going man, careful of the comfort of his passengers, and exceedingly fond of the game of brag. We had been out a little more than five days, and were in hopes of seeing the bluffs of Natchez on the next day. Our wood was getting low, and night coming on. The pilot on duty *above* (the other pilot held three aces at the time, and was just calling out the captain, who "went it strong" on three kings) sent down word that the mate had reported the stock of wood reduced to half a cord. The worthy captain excused himself to the pilot whose watch was *below* and the two passengers who made up the party, and hurried to the deck, where he soon discovered by the landmarks that we were about half a mile from a wood-yard, which he said was situated "right round yonder point."

221

"But," muttered the captain, "I don't much like to take wood of the yellow-faced old scoundrel who owns it; he always charges a quarter of a dollar more than any one else. However, there's no other chance." The boat was pushed to her utmost, and in a little less than an hour, when our fuel was about giving out, we made the point, and our cables were out and fastened to trees alongside of a good-sized wood-pile.

"Hallo, colonel! How d'ye sell your wood *this* time?"

A yellow-faced old gentleman with a two weeks' beard; strings over his shoulders holding up to his armpits a pair of copperas-colored linsey-woolsey pants, the legs of which reached a very little below the knee; shoes without stockings; a faded, broad-brimmed hat, which had once been black, and a pipe in his mouth—casting a glance at the empty guards of our boat, and uttering a grunt as he rose from fastening our "spring line," answered:

"Why, capting, we must charge you three and a quarter this time."

"The d——l!" replied the captain—captains did swear a little in those days—"what's the odd quarter for, I should like to know? You only charged me three as I went down."

"Why, capting," drawled out the wood merchant, with a sort of leer on his yellow countenance, which clearly indicated that his wood was as good as sold, "wood's riz since you went down, two weeks ago. Besides, you are awar that you very seldom stop, going *down*. When you're going *up* you're sometimes obleeged to give me a call, becaze the current's ag'inst you, and there's no other wood-yard for nine miles ahead; and if you happen to be nearly out of fooel, why——"

"Well, well," interrupted the captain, "we'll take a few cords, under the circumstances," and he returned to his game of brag.

In about half an hour we felt the *Caravan* commence paddling again. Supper was over, and I retired to my upper berth, situated alongside and overlooking the brag-table, where the captain was deeply engaged, having now the *other* pilot as his principal opponent. We jogged on quietly, and seemed to be going at a good rate.

"How does that wood burn?" inquired the captain of the mate, who was looking on at the game.

"'Tisn't of much account, I reckon," answered the mate; "it's cottonwood, and most of it green at that."

"Well, Thompson" ("Three aces again, stranger—I'll take that X and the small change, if you please. It's your deal.") —"Thompson, I say, we'd better take three or four cords at the next wood-yard; it can't be more than six miles from here." ("Two aces and a bragger, with the age! Hand over those V's.")

The game went on, and the paddles kept moving. At eleven o'clock it was reported to the captain that we were nearing the wood-yard, the light being distinctly seen by the pilot on duty.

"Head her inshore, then, and take in six cords, if it's good— see to it, Thompson. I can't very well leave the game now— it's getting right warm! This pilot's beating us all to smash."

The wooding completed, we paddled on again. The captain seemed somewhat vexed when the mate informed him that the price was the same as at the last wood-yard—three and a quarter—but soon again became interested in the game.

From my upper berth (there were no staterooms then) I could observe the movements of the players. All the contention appeared to be between the captain and the pilots (the latter personages took it turn and turn about, steering and playing brag), *one* of them almost invariably winning, while the two passengers merely went through the ceremony of dealing, cutting, and paying up their "antes." They were anxious to learn the game—and they *did* learn it! Once in a while, indeed, seeing they had two aces and a bragger, they would venture a bet of five or ten dollars, but they were always compelled to back out before the tremendous bragging of the captain or pilot; or, if they did venture to "call out" on "two bullits and a bragger," they had the mortification to find one of the officers had the same kind of a hand, and was more venerable! Still, with all these disadvantages, they continued playing; they wanted to learn the game.

At two o'clock the captain asked the mate how we were getting on.

"Oh, pretty glibly, sir," replied the mate; "we can scarcely tell what headway we *are* making, for we are obliged to keep the middle of the river, and there is the shadow of a fog rising. This wood seems rather better than that we took in at Yellow-Face's, but we're nearly out again, and must be looking out for more. I saw a light just ahead on the right. Shall we hail?"

"Yes, yes," replied the captain; "ring the bell, and ask 'em what's the price of wood up here." ("I've got you again; here's double kings.")

I heard the bell, and the pilot's hail, "What's *your* price for wood?"

A youthful voice on the shore answered, "Three *and* a quarter!"

"D—n it!" ejaculated the captain, who had just lost the price of two cords to the pilot—the strangers suffering *some* at the same time—"three and a quarter again! Are we never to get to a cheaper country?" ("Deal, sir, if you please; better luck next time.")

The other pilot's voice was again heard on deck:

"How much have you?"

"Only about ten cords, sir," was the reply of the youthful salesman.

The captain here told Thompson to take six cords, which would last till daylight, and again turned his attention to the game.

The pilots here changed places. When did they sleep?

Wood taken in, the *Caravan* again took her place in the middle of the stream, paddling on as usual.

Day at length dawned. The brag-party broke up and settlements were being made, during which operations the captain's bragging propensities were exercised in cracking up the speed of his boat, which, by his reckoning, must have made at least sixty miles, and would have made many more if he could have procured good wood. It appears the two passengers, in their first lesson, had incidentally lost one hundred and twenty dollars. The captain, as he rose to see about taking in some *good* wood, which he felt sure of obtaining now that he had got above the level country, winked at his opponent, the pilot, with whom he had been on very bad terms during the progress of the game, and said, in an undertone, "Forty apiece for you and I and James [the other pilot] is not bad for one night."

I had risen, and went out with the captain, to enjoy a view of the bluffs. There was just fog enough to prevent the vision taking in more than sixty yards; so I was disappointed in *my* expectation. We were nearing the shore for the purpose of looking for wood, the banks being invisible from the middle of the river.

"There it is!" exclaimed the captain; "stop her!" Ding, ding, ding, went the big bell, and the captain hailed:

"Hallo! the wood-yard!"

"Hallo yourself!" answered a squeaking female voice, which

came from a woman with a petticoat over her shoulders in place of a shawl.

"What's the price of wood?"

"I think you ought to know the price by this time," answered the old lady in the petticoat; "it's three and a qua-a-rter! and now you know it."

"Three and the d——l!" broke in the captain. "What, have you raised on *your* wood too? I'll give you *three*, and not a cent more."

"Well," replied the petticoat, "here comes the old man; he'll talk to you."

And, sure enough, out crept from the cottage the veritable faded hat, copperas-colored pants, yellow countenance and two weeks' beard we had seen the night before, and the same voice we had heard regulating the price of cottonwood squeaked out the following sentence, accompanied by the same leer of the same yellow countenance:

"Why, darn it all, capting, there is but three or four cords left, and since it's you, I don't care if I *do* let you have it for three—as you're a good customer!"

After a quick glance at the landmarks around, the captain bolted, and turned in to take some rest.

The fact became apparent—the reader will probably have discovered it some time since—that we had been wooding all night at the same wood-yard!

Marion Couthouy Smith

The Composite Ghost

THEY were placed on exhibition, in a long, imposing row,
All who'd borne the name of Spriggins for three centuries or
  so;
From old Amram, who came over in the Pilgrim Fathers'
  track,
To the late lamented Jane, for whom the family still wore black.
They stood upon a hardwood shelf, in rich and proud array,
Not disposed, I beg to state, in any grim, offensive way.
They were not a row of mummies, standing terrible and tall,
Nor a grisly stack of coffins, piled up high along the wall;
You never came across a skull, nor stumbled on a bone,
Nor a human frame in lattice-work, left rattling there alone;
Your nerves would never suffer there from sudden shocks or
  "turns"—
There was nothing but a score or two of classic little urns,
Which held their sacred contents, sealed in elegant reserve,
Like a ghastly kind of jam, or supernatural preserve.
You never, never would suspect that in those graceful rows
The entire Spriggins ancestry could peacefully repose.
'Tis a plan that's most convenient, thus within a little space,
To have your relatives condensed, and keep them in a vase;
For if you care to travel, why, wherever you may go,
You can simply take your family vault along with you, you
  know.
You can have the whole collection sent by Peterson's express,
To be a genteel solace in bereavement and distress.

Besides, it is the prettiest end a man could wish himself—
To be gathered to his fathers in an urn upon a shelf.

· · · · · ·

There rested all the Spriggins tribe, each in his little urn,
On which the names and dates were carved, as each had died
    in turn;
And Spriggins, *père*, was proud of them, and often went to
    weep
Beside the sacred shelf on which he one day hoped to sleep.
One fatal afternoon it chanced that Spriggins's youngest son,
Whose un-Christian age was seven, and whose Christian name
    was John,
Obtained the key to that small room, and found that sacred
    store
Of the ashes of his fathers, which he ne'er had seen before.
This Johnny was a clever boy, much given to research;
His very nose turned up, with interrogatory perch;
His head—excuse the slang—was very level, you'll surmise,
But 'twas level where his bump of veneration ought to rise.
He knew they were his relatives, within those vases packed,
But he didn't care a button for that interesting fact;
All he wanted was to reach those curious urns and take them
    down.
(Alas! the shelf was several feet above his little crown.)
There came a sudden avalanche, and flat upon the floor
He lay, sprinkled with the ashes of a century or more!
A portion of his grandpa ran in torrents down his neck,
And 'round him all his great-great-aunts were lying by the peck.
He had Pilgrim Fathers in his shoes, all trickling 'round his
    toes;
He had grandmas in his hair, and he had cousins in his nose;

And, worst of all, a fragment of the late lamented Jane
Had lodged beneath his eyelid, and was causing dreadful pain!
But John had lots of courage, and he didn't stop to cry,
Not even with the ashes of his sister in his eye;
He only gasped, and quickly rose, and ruefully surveyed
The ruin and confusion that his luckless fall had made.
He could sweep up all the ashes, but things never could be fixed,
For the worthy house of Spriggins was inextricably mixed!
Such stirring up would stagger e'en the very stoutest brain;
Why, you couldn't tell old Amram from the late lamented Jane.
The scions of this honored line, all by that little loon,
Might just as well have been stirred up, like pudding, with a
   spoon.
'Twas very sad; but Johnny, yielding not to thoughts of gloom,
Brought up a chair to stand on, and a dustpan and a broom,
And soon that little room was very, very cleanly swept,
And urns and ashes all put back, just where they had been kept.
You never, never would suspect what that one day had cost,
And that in that act each Spriggins's identity was lost!

   .   .   .   .

That night, alas! Pa Spriggins, in a solemn frame of mind,
Betook himself to that small room, as oft he felt inclined,
And he shut the door, and sat him down, those urns to con-
   template,
While appropriate reflections chased each other through his
   pate;
For he loved to pensively recount the treasures of the past,
And wondered constantly how long the family would last.
The place was dark and gloomy—he was shut up there alone,
When suddenly—his hair stood up!—he heard a hollow groan!
The cover of the largest urn rose up a little way,
A mist came forth, which altered to a figure dim and gray.

It rose up from the ashes, like the phenix known of old,
But of such an awful bird as this the ancients never told.
It bore a distant likeness to the figure of a man,
But picture such a nondescript I know I never can.
It had a gray old head upon the shoulders of a child;
One eye was small and wicked, and the other large and wild.
Its hands, its feet, its teeth, its ears, I solemnly declare,
You couldn't pick out two of them that matched to make a pair!
One foot was slim and dainty, and the other huge and flat,
And it had a woman's wig on underneath a man's cocked hat;
A waistcoat like George Washington's, a blazer and a train,
That Spriggins knew had once belonged to his departed Jane!
He sank upon his bended knees, with terror quite unmanned;
It stood upon its one large foot, and waved its biggest hand,
And spake: "Unhappy man," it said, "for this have we been
    burned?
For this have we been kept here long, so carefully inurned?
Oh, see, upon this sacred shelf what dire confusion reigns!
Wretch! what have you been doing with your ancestors' re-
    mains?
You listen to your father's voice, but thanks, I fear, to you,
It is your uncle Solomon whose mouth it's speaking through.
Oh, tell me who or what I am, and how long I've been dead;
And tell me if I've got my own or some one else's head;
I don't belong to any special period at all.
Am I my Aunt Kiziah, or am I your brother Paul?
Oh, Spriggins—Ebenezer J.!—Oh, wretch! Oh, fool! Oh,
    rash!
How could you mix your ashes in one vast, ancestral hash?"
Thus ending, with a mingled wail of misery and rage,
That awful vision ceased to speak, and vanished from the
    stage,

Marion Couthouy Smith

While ghostly groanings issued from the various urns around,
But poor old Spriggins heard no more—he swooned upon the
    ground.

· · ·

And now these mingled embers 'neath memorial marbles lie,
And Spriggins and his family will be buried when they die.

Alaric Bertrand Start

The Jim-Jam King of the Jou-Jous

An Arabian Legend

FAR off in the waste of desert sand,
The Jim-jam rules in the Jou-jou land:
He sits on a throne of red-hot rocks,
And moccasin snakes are his curling locks;
And the Jou-jous have the conniption fits
In the far-off land where the Jim-jam sits—
If things are nowadays as things were then.
Allah il Allah! Oo-aye! Amen!

The country's so dry in Jou-jou land
You could wet it down with Sahara sand,
And over its boundaries the air
Is hotter than 'tis—no matter where.
A camel drops down completely tanned
When he crosses the line into Jou-jou land—
If things are nowadays as things were then.
Allah il Allah! Oo-aye! Amen!

A traveler once got stuck in the sand
On the fiery edge of Jou-jou land;
The Jou-jous they confiscated him,
And the Jim-jam tore him limb from limb;
But, dying, he said: "If eaten I am,
I'll disagree with this Dam-jim-jam!
He'll think his stomach's a Hoodoo's den!"
Allah il Allah! Oo-aye! Amen!

Alaric Bertrand Start

Then the Jim-jam felt so bad inside,
It just about humbled his royal pride.
He decided to physic himself with sand,
And throw up his job in the Jou-jou land.
He descended his throne of red-hot rocks,
And hired a barber to cut his locks.
The barber died of the got-'em-again.
Allah il Allah! Oo-aye! Amen!

And now let every good Mussulman
Get all the good from this tale he can.
If you wander off on a jamboree
Across the stretch of the desert sea,
Look out that right at the height of your booze
You don't get caught by the Jou-jou-jous!
You may, for the Jim-jam's at it again.
Allah il Allah! Oo-aye! Amen!
                    —*Translated from the Arabic.*

William Henry McElroy

An Old War-Horse to a Young Politician

MY DEAR NEPHEW: I was seventy years old yesterday, and
although I feel as young as I ever did, I cannot shut my eyes to
the fact that in spite of my feelings I really am an old man.
So, since I must soon pass off the stage on which—if I say it
who shouldn't—I have long been a prominent figure, it is only
natural that I should desire, in the absence of a son of my own,
that my mantle should fall to a son of one of my blood. I
believe you have good stuff in you. Your valedictory when
you graduated, last summer, although containing too little that
was practical to suit my taste, would have done credit to the
average Cong—I was going to write Congressman; but I can
justly go further than that. It would have done credit to
the Washington journalists, who sometimes compose—that is
to say, revise—speeches for some of us Congressmen. This,
however, like the rest of my communication, is strictly between
ourselves.

When I left you, on Commencement Day, I urged you to lose
no time in getting into politics, promising that I would help you
push your fortunes as occasion offered. Since then I have
received a letter from you, in which you write that you have
read "Story of the Constitution," Benton's "Thirty Years in
the United States Senate," Greeley's "American Conflict,"
two or three works on political economy, and De Tocqueville
on America. I suppose there can be no objection to such
reading. Likely enough it has its value. But what I particularly desire, my dear nephew, is that you should become a

William Henry McElroy

practical politician—a thoroughly practical politician. I never remember reading any of the works you have mentioned, or any like them, unless, indeed, you call Barnum's "How to Make Money" a treatise on finance. And yet, cast your eyes over the salient points of my career. I have been alderman, supervisor, mayor, State representative, State senator, and Congressman. For many years I have been chairman of our State and county committees. I can hardly remember the time when I didn't carry the vote of my own ward in my vest-pocket and of my own city in my trousers-pocket, and I've got them there yet. For going on half a century I have had things pretty much my own way in caucuses and primaries, and the like. What has been the secret of my unusual success? I will try—in strict confidence, as you will understand—to give you some plain, blunt, non-partisan hints for your guidance in politics which may serve to answer the question.

I. Never allow yourself to lose sight of the fact that politics, and not poker, is our great American game. If this could be beaten into the heads of some presumably well-meaning but glaringly unpractical people, we should hear less idiotic talk about reform in connection with politics. Nobody ever dreams of organizing a reform movement in poker. How droll it would sound to read that "Hon. John Oakhurst, Hon. William Nye, and Hon. Ah Sin, in connection with other well-known citizens of California, are engaged in endeavoring to reform poker from the inside!" And yet political reform clubs, designed to reform politics from the inside or the outside, are springing up on all sides. Of course it is just as well not to attempt to argue the masses out of their deeply rooted notion that politics is what Noah Webster defines it to be, "that part of *ethics* which has to do with the regulation and government of a nation or state." Ethics is very good in connection with politics. But then Webster, it must be remembered, was simply a learned lexicographer, and not a practical politician. No, no. Don't try to reason with the masses in this matter. The public has no head for such things. It will not understand.

II. Mr. Lincoln, a very estimable and justly popular, but in some respects an impracticable man, formulated another widely diffused error in regard to politics. He held that ours is a government of the people, by the people, for the people. I maintain, on the contrary, that it is a government of politicians, by politicians, for politicians. If your political career is to be a success, you must understand and respect this distinction with a difference.

III. Not a few capable but unpractical people, when they fall to discussing our governmental system, argue that the existence of parties is necessary to the welfare of our country. But long experience has taught me that the more sensible way for a practical politician to look at it is that the existence of the country is necessary to the welfare of parties. Thank Heaven, my dear nephew, that we have a country!

IV. You have received your commission as postmaster of your village. A post-office is a capital political opening for a young man who has sense enough to discover how to make the right use of it. You will, of course, leave all matters touching the postal service to your deputy. Never forget that your pivotal duty as postmaster will be to nurse the party in your section. As a practical man, you must see, if you reflect a moment, that postmaster and local party master must be convertible terms with you if you expect to be approved by the great party leaders, and to become a great leader yourself some day. To be sure, if you find leisure, there can be nothing indelicate in your appearing at the post-office now and then and doing a few strokes of purely postal work. But take care that such service does not encroach upon the hours when you ought to be fostering the party boom. In your selection of clerks you will be guided primarily by a determination to have only such men around you as will register your will every time at caucuses and conventions. Should it turn out in any instance that you have been deceived in your man, be nice about the phrase with which you discharge him. I submit a formula which has been repeatedly tried, and generally found to work well. We will suppose the clerk who won't answer is named John Doe. You will call him into your private office and address him substantially as follows: "Mr. Doe, I am compelled with all reluctance, at the call of duty, to dissever our relations, and must request you to file your resignation forthwith. During your connection with this office as letter-carrier you have displayed an ability and a fidelity, a grace of manner and a strength of character, that have endeared you to all your associates, and done not a little to elevate the tone of the entire American postal service. If I have brought myself to part with you, it is solely to the end that there may be greater homogeneousness of view, so to speak, in the office." One of your predecessors used this formula with great satisfaction to himself, and apparently to those whom he decapitated. He always found, he told me, that the first part of it put the clerk to whom it was addressed in capital humor, while the "homogeneousness" dazed him to that extent that he walked out of the office minus his head, not appreciating what had been the matter, but having a nebulous impression that he had been killed by kindness.

V. I sincerely hope it is not necessary that I should counsel you always to vote the regular ticket, the whole regular ticket, and nothing but the regular ticket. Hold fast, I beseech of you, to the doctrine of the infallibility of your party in con-

vention assembled. Delegates, like kings, "can do no wrong."
The voters who scratch ballots or bolt nominations are to be
regarded as the bane of politics, just as certain other reformers
have been the bane of religion. They all belong in the same
category, and are all equally deserving of the execration of
every practical man, as exponents of the pestiferous doctrine
of the right of private judgment. And just here a word in
reply to the familiar question, Would you vote for the devil
if he received the party's regular nomination? I have no
hesitation in affirming that I certainly would. Let's look at it.
If the day ever comes when the devil is nominated, the other
side will be pretty sure to run Gabriel against him. Of the
two, my choice would be the devil. To be sure, it would not
be an ideal nomination, but, then, neither is ours an ideal world.
I am aware that the devil has split hoofs, pronounced horns,
and a bifurcated tail. But do we choose candidates for their
good looks? As to his moral character, I frankly admit it is
not all I could desire; but after criticism has exhausted itself,
the fact remains, conceded by both parties, that he is not as
black as he is painted. On the other hand, he has many
qualities that ought to commend him to practical men. He is
self-made, he is thoroughly in earnest in all he undertakes,
he is an untiring worker, he is one of the shrewdest of wire-
pullers, he possesses vast and versatile accomplishments, he is
unsurpassed in ability to find and manipulate the springs
that move men, he has a positive genius for making friends.
Gifted, popular, magnetic, at home in all circles, from the
highest to the lowest, he would be certain to make a splendid
run. As for Gabriel, I have only to say that, while his intellectual and moral endowments are undoubtedly of the
highest order, there is great reason to fear that he would not
succeed in the realm of practical politics. If elected to office,

William Henry McElroy

it is more than likely that he would prove more of a botheration than a boon to his party. He would be living up to the promises made during the canvass; he would resolutely decline to let well enough alone. Let me not be misunderstood. I yield to no one in my regard for Gabriel. But, as a practical man, I would feel called upon to vote against him, and do all I could for his opponent.

This communication has already exceeded reasonable limits, and yet I have only touched upon a few points. But perhaps I have written enough to start you right, to make you understand the nature of our great American game, and to put you in possession of the clue to the secret of playing it successfully. Be it yours to consult the expedient, leaving it to the purists of the party to consult the highly proper. Beware of those who take sentimental views of unsentimental matters. A man who would "rather be right than be President," by all means ought to decline a presidential nomination, and run for a position in a theological seminary, a Sunday-school, or Vassar College; while he who holds that "one with God is a majority" antagonizes the system of reckoning which has come down to us from the fathers, and which has the approval of every practical inspector of American elections. Be practical in your politics, be practical, evermore be practical.

With fervent hopes and high anticipations of your future, I subscribe myself your affectionate uncle,

————— ————.

To —— ——, Esq.

—*"Atlantic Monthly,"* 1880.

Carolyn Wells

The Poster Girl

THE blessed Poster Girl leaned out
  From a pinky-purple heaven;
One eye was red and one was green;
  Her bang was cut uneven;
She had three fingers on her hand,
  And the hairs on her head were seven.

Her robe, ungirt from clasp to hem,
  No sunflowers did adorn;
But a heavy Turkish portière
  Was very neatly worn;
And the hat that lay along her back
  Was yellow like canned corn.

It was a kind of wobbly wave
  That she was standing on,
And high aloft she flung a scarf
  That must have weighed a ton;
And she was rather tall—at least
  She reached up to the sun.

She curved and writhed, and then she said,
  Less green of speech than blue:
"Perhaps I *am* absurd—perhaps
  I *don't* appeal to you;
But my artistic worth depends
  Upon the point of view."

Carolyn Wells

I saw her smile, although her eyes
   Were only smudgy smears;
And then she swished her swirling arms,
   And wagged her gorgeous ears;
She sobbed a blue-and-green-checked sob,
   And wept some purple tears.

                 —*"Idle Idyls."*

The Tragedy of a Theater Hat

THE devil, one day, in a spirit of mirth,
Was walking around, to and fro, on the earth,
    When he heard a man say,
    In a casual way,
"I think I'll just drop in at the matinée;
For I feel in the humor to see a good play,
And the thing is a rattler, I've heard people say."
    The devil stood by,
    With a smile in his eye,
And he said, "I don't see any good reason why
I, too, shouldn't go to this play that's so fly."
Now, his Majesty, as is well known by the wise,
Assumes at his will any kind of disguise;
    And he said, "I will go
    To this wonderful show
In the shape of a man, and arrayed *comme il faut.*"
No sooner 'twas said than 'twas done, and away
His Majesty sped to the gay matinée.
In faultless attire becomingly garbed,
Concealing entirely his tail (which was barbed),

241

Correctly cravatted,
And duly silk-hatted,
With his two cloven hoofs patent-leathered and spatted,
He approached the box-office with jauntiest airs,
And purchased a seat in the orchestra chairs.
Then removing his tile,
He tripped down the aisle,
With a manner which showed no appearance of
    guile,
Although he could scarcely conceal a slight smile
As he noticed the ladies who sat near to him,
So modishly mannered, and quite in the swim—
The maidens so trim,
And the matrons so prim—
And he thought how extremely they'd be horrified
If they had any notion who sat by their side.
As his Majesty sat there enjoying it all,
There entered a lady exceedingly tall;
With a rustle of silk and a flutter of fur,
She sat herself down in the seat kept for her,
Right in front of Old Nick, and exactly between
Himself and the stage. And her insolent mien
Proclaimed her at once a society queen.
Her shoulders were broad, and supported a cape
Which gave you no clue to her possible shape,
'Twas so plaited and quilled,
And ruffled and frilled,
And it tinkled with bugles that never were stilled;
And wide epaulettes
All covered with jets,
Caught up here and there with enormous rosettes,
And further adorned with gold-spangled aigrettes.

Carolyn Wells

Encircling her neck was a boa of gauze,
Accordion-plaited and trimmed with gewgaws;
And perched on the top of her haughty, blonde head,
Was a HAT! Now, of course, you have all of you read
    Of the theater hats
    That are seen at the mats.,
That are higher than steeples and broader than flats;
But this one as far outshone all of the others
As young Joseph's dream-sheaves exceeded his brothers'.
'Twas a wide-rolling brim, and a high-peakéd crown,
And black feathers stood up and black feathers hung down;
And black feathers waved wildly in every direction,
Without any visible scheme of connection.
'Twas decked with rare flowers of a marvelous size,
And colors that seemed to bedazzle the eyes.
    And each vacant space
    Was filled in with lace,
And twenty-three birds in the ribbons found place.
And as this arrangement quite shut off his view,
The devil was nonplussed to know what to do.
And although he is not very often amazed,
Upon this occasion he found he was phased.
    But, looking around,
    He very soon found
That many fair ladies, as gorgeously gowned,
    Held their hats in their laps,
    Or still better, perhaps,
Had left them outside in the room with their wraps.
And assuming at once a society air,
He leaned over the back of the fair stranger's chair,
    And with manner well-bred,
    "Beg pardon," he said,

"Will you please take that awful thing off of your head?"
When, what do you think! The lady addressed
Indignantly stared, and politely expressed
A decided refusal to grant his request.

And the poor devil sat
Behind that big hat,
So mad that he didn't know where he was at.
He could not see a thing that took place on the stage,
And he worked himself into a terrible rage.

He murmured quite low—
But she heard him, you know—
"Lady, since you refused to remove that chapeau,
You're condemned now to wear it wherever you go.
Since you won't take it off when a duty you owe,

You shall not take it off when you wish to do so."

Alas for the lady! the devil has power,
And the rest of her life, from that terrible hour,
The curse of the devil compelled her to wear
That enormous beflowered and befeathered affair.
Her lot was a sad one. If you'll reckon o'er
The times when a hat is a terrible bore,

You'll certainly say
That to wear it all day
And then wear it all night is a fate to deplore.
She wore it at dinners, she wore it at balls;
She wore it at home when receiving her calls;
She wore it at breakfast, at luncheon, and tea;
Not even at prayers from that hat was she free.
She couldn't remove it on going to bed;
She rose, bathed, and dressed with that hat on her head.
If she lounged in the hammock, perusing a book,
Or went to the kitchen to speak to the cook,

Carolyn Wells

In summer or winter, the hat was still there,
And 'twas *so* in the way when she shampooed her hair.
Her lover would fain his fair sweetheart caress,
But who to his bosom could tenderly press
Twelve black, waving feathers and twenty-three birds?
He said what he thought, in appropriate words,
And broke the engagement. She vowed she would go
To a convent and bury her sorrow; but no—
They wouldn't receive her. It was the old tale,
That had quite prevented her taking the veil.
The curse was upon her! No mortal could save—
She carried that ill-fated hat to her grave.

MORAL

Now, all you young women with Gainsborough hats,
Beware how you wear them to Saturday mats.
  Remember the fate
  Of this maid up-to-date,
And take warning from her ere it may be too late.

From Carolyn Wells's "Idle Idyls," copyright by Life Publishing Company.

A Memory

How dear to this heart are the old-fashioned dresses,
 When fond recollection presents them to view!
In fancy I see the old wardrobes and presses
 Which held the loved gowns that in girlhood I knew.
The wide-spreading mohair, the silk that hung by it;
 The straw-colored satin with trimmings of brown;
The ruffled foulard, the pink organdy nigh it.

245

But, oh! for the pocket that hung in each gown!
 The old-fashioned pocket,
 The obsolete pocket,
  The praiseworthy pocket that hung in each gown.

That dear, roomy pocket I'd hail as a treasure,
 Could I but behold it in gowns of to-day;
I'd find it the source of an exquisite pleasure,
 But all my modistes sternly answer me "Nay."
'Twould be so convenient when going out shopping,
 'Twould hold my small purchases coming from town;
And always my purse or my kerchief I'm dropping.
 Oh, me! for the pocket that hung in my gown.
 The old-fashioned pocket,
 The obsolete pocket,
  The praiseworthy pocket that hung in my gown.

A gown with a pocket! How fondly I'd guard it!
 Each day ere I'd don it I'd brush it with care;
Not a full Paris costume could make me discard it,
 Though trimmed with the laces an empress might wear.
But I have no hope, for the fashion is banished;
 The tear of regret will my fond visions drown;
As fancy reverts to the days that have vanished,
 I sigh for the pocket that hung in my gown.
 The old-fashioned pocket,
 The obsolete pocket,
  The praiseworthy pocket that hung in my gown.

Carolyn Wells

One Week

THE year had gloomily begun
For Willie Weeks, a poor man's
> SUN.

He was beset with bill and dun,
And he had very little
> MON.

"This cash," said he, "won't pay my dues;
I've nothing here but ones and
> TUES."

A bright thought struck him, and he said,
"The rich Miss Goldrocks I will
> WED."

But when he paid his court to her,
She lisped, but firmly said, "No,
> THUR!"

"Alas!" said he, "then I must die!"
His soul went where they say souls
> FRI.

They found his gloves, and coat, and hat,
The Coroner upon them
> SAT.
> —*"Idle Idylls."*

The *A B C* of *Literature*

A IS for Anthony Hope,
Who gives to his fancy free scope;
     In turret and tower
     His characters cower,
Or make hairbreadth escapes by a rope.

B is for bashful James Barrie,
From the land of the kilt and Glengarry;
     We've read him to date,
     And his next we await,
For we wonder whom Tommy will marry.

C is for colorful Crane,
Who has a phenomenal brain;
     His language amazes,
     He writes in blue blazes,
And his verses are really insane.

D is for R. Harding Davis,
And jolly good stories he gave us;
     Van Bibber will do,
     And Gallagher, too,
But from his war-notes the saints save us.

E is for George Egerton,
Whose "Keynotes" were rather good fun;
     But her themes pathologic,
     And terms pedagogic,
Are things the young persons should shun.

Carolyn Wells

F is for Frances Burnett,
Who revels in plain epithet;
    Her people of quality,
    Though given to jollity,
Are the worst that we ever have met.

G is for Mr. Grant Allen,
Who pours out his views by the gallon;
    His books are improper,
    But he's a Hill-topper,
So he fears not the critic's sharp talon.

H is William Dean Howells,
As wise as the wisest of owls;
    The subject of jokes
    Of frivolous folks,
At which he good-naturedly growls.

I is for Ian Maclaren,
Who knows about Moses and Aaron;
    But in stories and tales
    He signally fails,
For of artistic interest they're barren.

J is for jimp Henry James,
Who expounds lofty motives and aims
    With sentences long
    And arguments strong,
And the most unpronounceable names.

K is for capable Kipling,
Who, though he's accounted a stripling,
    Writes stories and rimes
    Right up to the times
About loving and fighting and tippling.

L is for lean Andrew Lang,
Who recently saw, with a pang,
    That a man up in Maine
    Stole the work of his brain,
And he gave him a lengthy harangue.

M is Maurice Maeterlinck,
Whose dramas are graveyards in ink;
    Abstract, esoteric,
    Symbolic, hysteric—
To read him would drive us to drink.

N is for noxious Nordau,
Who pictures the terrible wo
    In store for the race
    Since we've fallen from grace,
And surely the Doctor should know.

O is for Miss Olive Schreiner,
Whose writings grow finer and finer;
    She certainly seems
    To be given to dreams
Of which she's the only diviner.

Carolyn Wells

P is for Popular Parker,
Who writes of the North, where it's darker;
     His "Pretty Pierre"
     Is drawn with great care,
But to "Valmond" he isn't a marker.

Q is for quick-witted "Q,"
At home on a staff or a crew;
     With vigor and skill
     He handles a quill,
Or paddles his well-loved canoe.

R is for Richard Le Gallienne,
Who really deserves a medallion
     That his "Fancies" and "Quest"
     Were never suppressed;
But they ought to be writ in Italian.

S is for sad Sarah Grand,
Who marital happiness banned;
     Her public she vexes
     With problems of sexes
Which most of us can't understand.

T is for terse Thomas Hardy,
Whose works we with wonder regard. He
     Has written for years,
     But it somehow appears
His moral convictions were tardy.

American Wit and Humor

U is for dear Uncle Remus,
To praise him 'twould surely beseem us;
    We've contracted a habit
    Of quoting Br'er Rabbit,
Or poor old Br'er Wolf *in extremis*.

V is for Victoria Crosse,
Who wouldn't be much of a loss,
    For her "Woman Who Wouldn't"
    Or Couldn't or Shouldn't,
Is nothing but driveling dross.

W is Mrs. Ward,
By whom we are awfully bored;
    "Robert Elsmere" we stood,
    And "Marcella" was good,
But when "Tressady" came we were floored.

X is the author unknown,
Who signs any name but his own;
    And though nobody claims
    "The Descendant" and "James,"
In their pages good writing is shown.

Z is for Zangwill the Zealous,
Of whom our own critics are jealous,
    But in epigram keen,
    Free from malice or spleen,
Those foreigners seem to excel us.

College Humor

Won the Pot

THAT little hand!
I hold it firm in mine,
And scan its outlines fine.
    My eyes expand,
And grow with love intense and strong;
I gaze upon it fond and long,
    That little hand!

That little hand!
It is so smooth, so pure and white,
And covered o'er with diamonds quite,
    In beauty grand.
Oh, how I love it! See me press
It to my lips in fond caress,
    That little hand!

That little hand!
There are no others fair as you!
I lay you down, and gladly too,
    With manner bland.
It was a diamond flush and straight!
Soon may I hold its charming mate!
    That little hand!
                    —J. R., in *The Columbia Spectator.*

The Rocks of Mt. Desert

THE soft light of the setting sun
  Across the water lay,
And dark against its glory rose
  The islands of the bay;
The air was still, upon the shore
  The pine-trees stood inert,
The quiet sea broke softly on
  The rocks of Mt. Desert.

The placid water mirrored back
  The glory of the skies,
But all the glow I heeded not
  For the light of two soft eyes;
And often as, so slightly raised,
  They did to mine revert,
No paradise, I felt, was like
  The rocks of Mt. Desert.

The murmuring sea I did not hear,
  For a voice of music sweet
That thrilled my heart, until I thought
  I almost heard it beat;
For all was still, upon the shore
  The pine-trees stood inert,
No sighing breezes swept across
  The rocks of Mt. Desert.

College Humor

The sunset died, the sobbing sea
　I heard along the shore;
That thrilling voice, those tender eyes,
　Are gone forevermore.
She is not dead or gone away,
　The fickle little flirt,
But glorifies, to other eyes,
　The rocks of Mt. Desert.
　　　　—E. M. T., in *The Columbia Spectator*.

Mutability

WHEN lips are cherry-red,
　When eyes are blue,
"Vision of loveliness"
　I think—don't you?

When eyes are cherry-red,
　And lips are blue,
"Some one's been on a bat,"
　I think—don't you?
　　　　—*The Morningside*, Columbia.

A College Widow

PRETTY? Rather! Her teeth were like pearls, sir,
　Peeping out between coralline bars;
And her eyes, when she smiled on a fellow,
　Just twinkled like midnight cigars.

255

She captured our whole delegation—
  A Trinity junior (a swell),
Two cheeky sub-freshmen from Harvard,
  And a couple of sophs from Cornell.

Well, we used to walk out in the evening
  To watch the moon's crescent arise;
And some of us thought of the landscape,
  But the rest of us thought of her eyes.
And when on the murmuring water
  The silvery light was aglow,
It appeared like a vision of Eden
  (To the freshmen especially so).

Such is life! Here, I'll show you the locket
  She gave me at parting; and Will
Has a bangle of hers in his pocket—
  We keep them for memorabil'.
As for me, though, I wasn't enraptured,
  In spite of the rose-tint and pearl,
For somehow I'm never contented
  With only a tenth of a girl.

And she's not very young, let me tell you—
  Ten years since they shipped her from school;
And I don't think she'll ever get married,
  She can't find a big enough fool.
Her name? Miss Van Arsdel, of Brooklyn.
  You met her, you say, in July?
You're engaged to her, Tom? Oh, the dickens!
  Beg par— I—well, hang it—good-by!
          —Anonymous, in *Acta Columbiana.*

L'Envoi

WHEN earth's last hazard is taken, and the last opportunity
   teed,
When the smoothest greens are deserted, and the youngest
   caddy has "deed,"
We shall rest, and, faith, we shall need it—burn golf clubs and
   caddy bag, too,
Till the Master of all good golfers shall put us to play anew.

And those that played par shall be happy; they shall golf o'er
   the starry fair;
They shall clear each heavenly bunker with never a need to
   swear;
They shall find no bogies to beat them, and shall lower them
   every one;
They shall never top, slice, or foozle, and the duffer shall never
   be done.

And only the Master shall praise us, and only the Master shall
   blame;
And no one shall play for the gallery, and no one shall play for
   fame,
But each for the joy of golfing, and each on a star for a tee,
Shall call "fore" to an angel caddy, content that the Master
   should see.

   —*"The Seven Tees," by K-pl-ng*, W. S. (Columbia).

To My Meerschaum

THERE'S a charm in the sun-crested hills,
  In the quivering light of a star,
In the plash of a silvery rill,
  Yet to me thou art lovelier far,
                My meerschaum!

There's a love in her witching dark eye,
  There's a love in her tresses at play,
Yet her love would be worth not a sigh,
  If from thee she could call me away,
                My meerschaum!

Let revelers sing of their wine,
  As they toss it in ecstasy down,
But the bowl I call for is thine,
  With its deepening amber and brown,
                My meerschaum!

For when trouble would bid me despair,
  I call for a flagon of beer,
And puff a defiance to care,
  Till sorrows in smoke disappear,
                O meerschaum!

Though 'mid pleasures unnumbered I whirl,
  Though I traverse the billowy sea,
Yet the waving and beautiful curl
  Of thy smoke's ever dearer to me,
                My meerschaum!
                —P. D. R., in *Acta Columbiana.*

From the Rubaiyat of Mr. Hennessy

WHIN I was young I give a lot of t'ought
　To all this High Serblime, an' sich like rot;
And now I know jist what I knew before;
　Mebbe it's thrue, me b'y—mebbe it's not.

There's them that lays up threasure in the sky
　They'll never see—they'll niver git that high.
Ah, Terence, don't ye listen to no band
　Ten blocks away, playin' "Swate by an' by."

Some Dill's cut plug, a pipe ye've smoked before,
　A wild young t'ing to kiss behind the door,
An' now an' thin an avenin' wit' the dhrink—
　Sure, what the divil wud ye ask wit' more?

Fill up the can, thin, an' we'll send it back;
　Man, don't be t'inkin' of all the t'ings ye lack;
Ye know this ain't no long job, annyway,
　An' any minnit we may get the sack.
　　　　　　—B. P. FOUR, in *East and West* (Columbia).

The Retort Courteous

THE master had come into the life class that morning in a more than ordinarily savage mood. He bullied the model and scolded the students. As he criticized his way down the room his comments became more severe and his voice louder, until sympathetic souls began to wonder what would happen when he came to Carol Dinwiddie. Carol Dinwiddie was a Southern girl, a girl with wide, innocent blue eyes, and thin, scarlet lips. Her face was delicate, almost to sharpness, with that ethereal, other-world sort of beauty that is almost painful to look at. She had little talent and less training, and her fellow students were used to hearing the master's choicest sarcasm lavished upon her work. She received these criticisms in meek silence, but with a look of hurt surprise that would have melted any other man into a kindly lie. To-day her work was worse than usual. The master paused behind her chair for one speechless moment, then, pointing at her unlucky sketch, thundered out, "What-in-the-devil is that?"

Carol Dinwiddie looked up at him from her saintlike halo of loose golden hair, and responded in her soft, Southern drawl, "What-in-hell do you think it is?"

GRACE GOODALE—*The Morningside*, Columbia University.

At the Eighth Tee

BILLY STALLMAN is my cousin, and I have never had any delusions regarding the evenness of his temper. Consequently, in company with his other well-meaning friends, I have always tried to keep him away from golf. You see, Billy is one of the best-hearted fellows in the world, but his disposition is of a decidedly rocket-like nature. He declares that he is the most reasonable man on earth, and asks only that people and things behave in a sensible, logical fashion. But when he runs up against a man who can't see his reasonable point of view, or against some illogical perversity in inanimate objects, he is really apt to throw things around. Any one who has ever tried a single game of golf will understand why we trembled at the thought of Billy's taking up the game. We didn't care to have the air full of hurtling clubs; nor did we wish our caddies—who were really not a very annoying lot, as caddies go—to come to violent and untimely ends.

But no man who visits the Moreland Country Club can be kept away from the links, and Billy fell at last into the clutches of the game. It was the old story. He was standing one day by the first tee, watching his friend Robertson foozling off some wretched shots, and freely expressing his astonishment over the man's stupidity at such an apparently simple trick. At last the exasperated Robertson thrust a driver into Billy's hand and bade him do better himself. Billy grasped the club with the beginner's gingerly awkwardness, stepped to the tee, and batted at the ground with the fiercest energy. And the ball—most perverse of atoms—"lit out" from the tee in a low, screaming curve, a full hundred and eighty yards, straight over the circular bunker that guards the first green—the finest drive made from that tee in a month.

"You see," said Billy calmly, "I told you it was easy. Here, take your club; I've had enough."

"No, no, old man," urged Robertson, yearning for revenge, "try it again. Why, you're a perfect genius at it! Here's another ball."

Thus urged, Billy drew back and struck again, and again, and again—six times, in fact—and plowed up all the tee within a radius of three feet, and fanned the whistling air; while the ball sat calmly and exasperatingly motionless on its little mound of sand. Then Billy paused, and looked up to heaven, and delivered himself of a speech whose ornamentations I will omit.

"Why, confound it all!" he declaimed, "I hit it exactly the same way I did at first. Why don't it go? There's no logic *in* it!"

Then, with careful precision, he smashed the driver over his knee, and hurled it afar.

"Blast the game!" he vowed. "I'll find out why I can't hit the thing, if I smash every club in New York!"

So Billy was trapped, you see, just the way so many have been taken. He really got along much better than we had expected. True, his bill at the club-maker's was abnormally large, and his exclamations in sand-bunkers were not always fit for the public ear; while his wrathful orders to his caddies would have reduced less hardened youths to tears. But he was always so jolly and kind-hearted to these same boys as soon as the round was over, and he used to tip them so generously for club cleaning (quite contrary to the rules of the Green Committee), and present them with so many old clubs, that they became his devoted admirers, and would endure his most violent abuse with entire equanimity, and often a quiet grin. Billy stuck at the game most persistently. He often used to go out for a lonely round before breakfast, and come in quite pale with rage. But at last, as a man can't stay in a white heat all the time, he got so that he could play with tolerable calmness and real good nature, except under extraordinary circumstances. Though the maddening unreasonableness of the game was still occasionally too much for him, he settled down into a fairly steady golfer, and even won a cup or two.

Thus a year and more passed. Then came an unusually heavy winter, and for weeks the links of the Moreland Country Club were deep in snow or slush. Having thus much idle time on his hands, Billy, who had hitherto never cared much for girls' society, must needs go and fall in love and get engaged. Whereat all his cynical friends—men, I mean, of course—shook their heads in skeptical despair, and declared that, though a man of Billy's temper might possibly learn to put up with the unreasonableness of golf, the unreasonableness of woman he could never, never endure. All this was very unfair to Eleanor Markham, for, in the first place, Billy seemed fond enough of her to stand a good deal of illogicality, and then she wasn't really unreasonable—few women are—but just rather impulsive and hasty.

When the golfing season opened again, Miss Markham, who put up a tolerably good game, naturally proposed that she and Billy should enter the mixed handicap foursome for the pair of silver loving-cups. In case you happen not to know—though that seems hardly possible—let me inform you that in a mixed foursome each pair, which is made up of a man and a woman, has but one ball, and the two strike at it in turn. As one generally spends the time getting the ball into trouble, and the other endeavoring to get it out, the game is very trying on the dispositions of both. But, you see, Miss Markham had never played golf with Billy, and hadn't a cousin's knowledge of his temper. So the two entered.

Jack Schuyler and I were paired with them, and up to the eighth hole on the first round the four of us had a very jolly time. Billy's temper was positively sunny, for both good form and good luck were with him and his partner that day. The first seven holes had cost them only forty-one strokes, which, considering their handicap of ten, gave them a remarkably good chance at the cups—provided only that they kept up a steady game. Now just in front and a little to the right of the eighth tee on the Moreland links is the only water-hazard—a muddy, ominous-looking pond, which has been the death of many a record score. Before Miss Markham and I drove, Billy very foolishly gave his partner some parting instructions.

"Now, Eleanor," said he cheerily, "we've got the best sort of show of winning these cups, and we *must* get them. All we've got to do is to play safe. Now, don't try to carry the pond. Play over to the left. Just give me a good lie on the fair green there, and I'll put the ball right up by the hole. To the left, remember!"

When Miss Markham drove she *did* face to the left, I could see that; but unluckily (you know the way one often does when there's a hazard in front) she sliced her ball away off to the right. It rose high in one of those sickly, irritating curves, and dropped—chug!—right into the middle of the pond. Miss Markham didn't say a word; she just shut her lips tight.

There was an ominous silence when Billy came back to have his try at it. Luck was certainly with him, for he carried the pond cleanly with a good, straight ball. Then he turned to Miss Markham.

"Two strokes thrown away!" he groaned. "Good heavens, Eleanor, why *did* you aim for the pond? Why didn't you go up to the left, as I told you?"

I started to move away, for I hate quarrels, and I knew Miss Markham's state of mind.

"My dear Billy," she returned, with slow, calm sarcasm, "do you suppose I stood up there and deliberately aimed for the middle of the pond and put the ball there because I wanted to?"

Billy gave a disagreeable, sneering little laugh. "Well," said he quickly, "it looked something like it. Unless you'd turned around and driven backward, you couldn't very well have sent the ball farther from the direction I told you to put it."

Miss Markham's lip curled scornfully. "You surely don't suppose I'd intentionally disregard the instructions of such an authority as you are. Of course *your* ball never goes in any other direction than the one you intend it to. *You* never put balls in the pond."

She must have heard of Billy's long catalogue of disasters on that hole.

"I can't see that that affects the argument," snapped out Billy, in exasperation. "But, at least, when *I* aimed for the pond just now I carried it, and didn't plump the ball into the middle, the way you did."

"Quite true," returned Miss Markham freezingly. "When I suggested that we enter together I didn't appreciate what an accomplished expert I was going to play with. Now that I see you make such drives as this, I appreciate my incompetence. I fear we're quite unfitted to be partners." And with this meaning remark she turned her back on Billy and walked on toward the ball, swinging her club haughtily.

The rest of the game was very embarrassing. Jack Schuyler and I tried to keep up some semblance of sociable gaiety, but the other two tramped after their ball in cold silence. Billy soon tried to speak to Miss Markham, but she promptly froze him into discouragement and silence, broken only by an occasional berating of his caddie.

Strangely enough, they continued to make a fairly good score. Billy, especially, played the game of his life just because he didn't care a straw how he played, I suppose. In spite of his fine strokes, he walked along in melancholy wretchedness. His irritation had, as usual, soon vanished. Though he felt that his position had not been illogical, he knew he oughtn't to have lost his temper. Besides, he was, as I have remarked, really very fond of Miss Markham, and unspeakably depressed at the thought of a prolonged period of coldness between them. So, during all the first part of the second round, he tried to think of some way of conciliating her. As we were on the seventh hole a fixed idea slowly took possession of his brain.

"Of course," he reasoned, "it naturally irritates Eleanor to see me play so well after what we've said; particularly as *she* isn't quite up to her game. I seem to be setting myself up as a sort of infallible golfing prig. And if I make a good drive over the pond this round, after *her* foozle before, it'll just be the last straw. Well, I won't. I'll just plunk right into the old pond. And then she can pitch into me, and she'll see I'm not a bit better than she is. That'll make her feel much better, and we'll laugh it all off and get on good terms again."

As we all walked up to the eighth tee, Billy couldn't help doing some silent calculation. "Fifty-three for the first round, in spite of the two strokes lost, and only forty-two for seven holes of the second. Why, if they got these last two holes in a tolerably low score, they had the cups sure! But never mind," reasoned Billy, "I'd rather lose the match and be on good terms with Eleanor. I think my plan's perfectly logical. Now, I'll just press, and top this ball right into the middle of the pond."

So Billy stepped on the tee and looked across at the hole, which is about two hundred yards away. Then he deliberately broke every rule of correct driving. He shut his eyes, swung with every ounce of his strength, and jerked frantically upward, intending to hit the ball on top, rolling it into the water in front.

To his horror, he felt a springy snap as his club caught the ball clean and fair, and he opened his eyes to see a white speck whistling over the corner of the pond, straight toward the hole, striking some yards short of the green, bounding, rolling on toward the flag, finally creeping up within three feet of the hole, where it stopped. Billy stood aghast, horror and despair on his face. To think that his most determined efforts for a foozle should be rewarded by the finest drive of the day! Alas! the hideous unreasonableness of golf had ruined his plan. Surely, after this, Eleanor would *never* forgive him.

As Billy stepped angrily from the tee, Miss Markham at last removed her eyes from the ball, with a gasp of relief and delight; and then (I told you she was impulsive) she threw her arms around Billy's neck and kissed him. "Oh, Billy, Billy!" she cried. "What a *superb, magnificent* drive! I'd just been counting up, and I knew that if we got this hole fairly well we'd have the cups surely. Oh, Billy, if you'd sent it into the pond I'd never have forgiven you, never, never!"

For a moment I don't think Billy was even pleased. He just looked discouraged.

"Good Lord!" he groaned. "What with a combination of golf and girls, what's the use of a man's *trying* to be logical?"

But the next second he realized his good luck; for he was, as I have remarked, really very fond of Miss Markham.

So Jack Schuyler helped me build my tee while they made it all up. The caddies couldn't see; they were fishing for balls down by the pond.

Miss Markham holed the three-foot put, and, with a two in their score, they naturally won the silver loving-cups, though they really didn't deserve them. If Jack Schuyler and I hadn't had such hard luck on the fifth hole— But that's just the way of golf.

However, I was glad to see Billy's temper get out of the first break so successfully. But I tremble for the future. Golf and a girl do seem to make a dangerous combination for a man of his disposition.

V. C. G.—*The Morningside*, Columbia University.

Freshman Themes No. 2—Thanksgiving

THANKSGIVING was originated by our New England ancestors in order that once a year they might get into a true, pious, Puritanical gloom. To this end they invented the New England mince pie and the Plymouth Rock chicken—the former to produce gloom inside; the latter to aid in the general effect by causing unpleasant fatigue of the jaw muscles. Their degenerate descendants have, however, done away with this latter feature, and the above-mentioned adamantine fowl has been replaced by the more easily chewed turkey. The pie, however, still remains, and the Great Pie Belt still marks the westward course of the Mayflower blood. In it pies are still eaten at breakfast, lunch, dinner, supper, and between meals by their pious and gloomy devotees. The only relaxation permitted on Thanksgiving was kicking Quakers around the lot, from which has developed the modern football game. The name Thanksgiving, according to John Fiske, originally referred to the day after, and indicated how glad they were it was all over; but other authorities regard it as an example of grim Puritan irony.—*The Columbia Jester.*

A Coincidence

GRANDMOTHER sits in her old armchair,
   Placidly knitting the hours away;
Kindly, yet grave, with her silvered hair,
   Tracing the cares of life's yesterday.

College Humor

Granddaughter cozily kneels beside,
　Resting an elbow on grandma's knee,
Pondering how she can best confide
　Something momentous, 'tis plain to see.

On goes the click of the ivory bones,
　Till dainty fingers obstruct the view,
And a shy voice asks in coaxing tones,
　"Tell me how grandpa proposed to you."

Down drops the knitting and truant ball,
　While grandma answers, 'twixt smile and tear,
"Grandfather never proposed at all;
　Somehow we knew it without, my dear."

Granddaughter blushes a dainty pink,
　Keeping her gaze fixed on grandma's knee.
"Isn't it funny," she says, "to think
　It is just that way with Jack and me?"
　　　　　—F. T. Cooper, in *The Harvard Lampoon.*

Cross-Purposes

We have paused to watch the quiver
Of faint moonbeams on the river,
　　By the gate.
We have heard something calling,
And a heavy dew is falling,
　　Yet we wait.

269

It is, no doubt, very silly
To stay out in all this chilly
    Evening mist;
Still I linger, hesitating,
For her lips are plainly waiting
    To be kissed.

So I stoop to take possession
Of the coveted concession
    On the spot;
But she draws back with discreetness,
Saying, with tormenting sweetness,
    "I guess not."

Her whole manner is provoking:
"Oh, well, I was only joking,"
    I reply.
She looks penitently pretty,
As she answers, "What a pity!
    So was I."
    —F. T. COOPER, in *The Harvard Lampoon*.

Capriciousness

DURING a pause from a breathless dance,
Somewhat withdrawn from mama's keen glance,
Out of the ballroom's fatiguing glare,
In safe seclusion and cooler air,
Curtained from view by the window-lace,
Stands a sweet vision of girlish grace—
Fluttering drapery of gauzy white—
Eyes like the depths of a summer night;

Four hands confusingly interlaced,
Protective coat sleeve around her waist,
Glance so alluring and smile so rash,
Threatening approach of a bold mustache;
Wilfully tossing her dainty head,
"Some one is looking this way," she said.

Slipping mischievously out of reach,
Yet half repenting her wilful speech;
Watching results with a vague alarm,
Wholly released from his willing arm;
Looking as shy as a sweet wild rose,
With the soft color that comes and goes;
And dainty fingers, set free, now fain
To be close prisoners o'er again,
Turning half nervously in and out;
Ruby lips arched to a tempting pout,
Secretly longing to say enough
To make amends for the late rebuff—
Penitently, and with drooping head,
"No one is looking just now," she said.

—F. T. Cooper, in *The Harvard Lampoon.*

A University Catechism

Compiled for Sub-Freshmen and Members of the Professional Schools

Q. What is a university?
A. I do not know.
Q. You are quite right. Who does know?
A. Nobody in America, though some people think they do.

Q. What are the objects of a university?

A. To unfit people for practical life.

Q. To whom do you refer by "people"?

A. I refer to the teachers and students alike.

Q. And what are the effects of a university?

A. To unfit the same people for life here or hereafter. This, however, is of little importance, as a university teaches that there is no life hereafter.

Q. Then a university effects more than is intended?

A. Much.

Q. What is necessary to make a university?

A. Money.

Q. Anything else?

A. Yes; a mixture of assurances and self-con——

(The rest of the catechism has been, for some unexplained reason, suppressed by the faculty.)—*The Harvard Lampoon.*

Extra !

Ghastly Scenes in the Anatomical Lab on Hallowe'en

Three Stiffs Limber Up for a Few Hours—They are Interviewed by Our Ghost Editor, Resulting in the Explanation of the Mysterious Disappearance of Messrs. Grind, Half-back, and Shy-frat—Another Great Scoop Credited to *Wrinkle.*

It was an awful night.

So, at least, thought all upper-classmen who happened to be out so late. So thought all juniors who happened to be in so early. So thought each of some six hundred little freshmen as he lay tucked snugly in his little bed, listening to the whistling of the wind, and sobbing softly to himself. The air was charged (for even that is charged in Ann Arbor) with electricity; and the rain fell in such torrents that Pieface was as dough before it.

It was growing very late. The library was dark, but that doesn't prove anything; and Jolly and Tuttle were watching each other to see who could close up first. The night was wearing on rapidly, and the streets became more and more deserted.

About twelve o'clock, when the festive boarding-house cook was beginning to pound the steak for breakfast, Sporter, our ghost editor, passed like a shadow up the street and rapidly made his way toward the anatomical lab. His managing editor had felt vague premonitions that there were to be mysterious manifestations on that part of the campus; and with the intention of scooping the *Bulletin, Inlander,* and *University Record,* he had sent his best man to investigate.

He could not have made a better selection. Sporter was almost fearless. He believes in ghosts, and had deadheaded his way all his life. Realizing that his mission was a particularly grave one, he had brought his spiritual adviser with him, from which, from time to time, he took copious drafts.

Reaching the lab, he inserted a skeleton key into the door and entered. Once inside, his nerve almost forsook him; and well it might. He found himself in a room containing an immense vat which held a half-dozen bodies properly tagged and prepared for the dissection table. These were the subjects he had to interview.

As the bell in the library tolled twelve, there was a slight stir in the vat; then a sepulchral sigh or two, mingled with wild wailings and low moans. Sporter's hair turned red with fright and his teeth usurped his tongue.

Presently, with a loud splash, the cover of the tank was pushed up, and three cadaverous beings, with glazed eyes and faces streaming with brine, rose to the side of the tank, tumbled over to the floor, and lay there motionless.

Sporter advanced and offered his card. The cadavers were a little stiff at first, but as their circulation was resumed they became quite communicative.

"To think I should come to this!" said one, as he pointed a bloated finger at a table on which lay a half-dissected body.

"Two weeks ago I was playing half-back on the 'varsity eleven. It was the Minnesota game, you know, and I was to have the ball. The signal was given; I started. The entire Minnesota eleven jumped on me, and here I am."

"But didn't the Michigan men interfere?" said Sporter indignantly.

"Nay," said Half-back with a sigh. "It is one of their fixed rules never to interfere with one another's playing, and I did not know that hatchets were allowed under this year's rules." He choked back some embalming fluid, and continued: "The idea of this being the goal of all my hopes! I don't want to be pessimistic, but I can't help kicking at it. My death, however, was quite inexpensive. The Minnesotas laid me out, and the athletic association realized on my body. I hope they will apply the money in securing a new ambulance, for the laundry wagon they now use is not up to date."

"And you," said Sporter, turning with great interest toward the second, "what is your history?"

"I was a grind," said the second stiff meditatively, as he toyed with a prof's eye that had been knocked out that morning. "Grammatically, the past of grind is ground; and logically I should have been buried. But here I am, and there is no use being cut up about it until I have to be. I used to study twenty-two hours a day; I rarely wasted more than five minutes at a meal, and never indulged in any such nonsense as exercise. When they told me I was getting stoop-shouldered, I replied that I stooped to conquer, and they let me alone after that. I always learned everything by heart—never tried to reason anything out; and if a question arose that was not in the lesson, I was not in it. I never took any interest in university affairs, for that takes time; and I never supported any university organization, for that takes money. I never swore, smoked, told a lie, nor kissed a pretty girl. I was a model—a clay one, now," and he laughed a hollow, spasmodic laugh. "Well, I grew to be such a dig that I almost dug myself a grave, and now I find myself in a pretty pickle." At this he nodded toward the vat. The Grind was silent.

Sporter, almost beside himself with excitement, looked long and earnestly at the third stiff. He felt sure that he had seen him before. A mutual recognition followed, and the cadaver extended two fingers of his left hand to Sporter.

"Ah, yes," he said, "I remember you. We met at Parker's, don't you know? I was a Shy-frat, at least I would have been one if I hadn't died of the grip. They taught me to bow by holding out my hat as if waiting for a coryphée to kick it, and made me practise walking with my cane in my mouth. When they initiated me, I had to swear not to drink any water or to be civil to an independent, except when I wanted to borrow his essay or examination papers; and I was not to bolt less than twice a week. But I'd rather be here than in the graveyard. Such swell company, you know."

As he finished, a cock in the distance crew thrice. At the last crow the three cadavers grew stiff. Their eyes became as stones, and they sank lifeless to the floor while trying to climb back into the vat.

Sporter gathered up his notes and made a sneak for the door. When outside, he breathed more freely, took a long pull at his spiritual adviser, and disappeared among the sighing trees.

—*Wrinkle*, University of Michigan.

A Lovely Scene

WE stood at the bars as the sun went down
　　Beneath the hills on a summer day;
Her eyes were tender and big and brown,
　　Her breath as sweet as the new-mown hay.

Far from the west the faint sunshine
　　Glanced sparkling off her golden hair;
Those calm, deep eyes were turned toward mine,
　　And a look of contentment rested there.

I see her bathed in the sunlight flood,
　　I see her standing peacefully now,
Peacefully standing and chewing her cud,
　　As I rubbed her ears—that Jersey cow.

—ANONYMOUS, in *Harvard Advocate*.

A Silent Partner

"ISN'T it weird? Don't you think West Point cadets are just too splendid for words? And is this the new field? Oh, isn't it ravishing? And they are the dormitories at this end. I

think it is so nice that the men can just sit at their windows
and see all the— Were you saying something? Oh, it
isn't the dormitories. How disappointing! Now, don't laugh.
Everybody laughs at me. I make the most inane mistakes.
Do you know, when I was at Florence's luncheon yesterday—
Are these our seats? Is that Captain Farnsworth? Isn't
he just a dream? He must look so nice in his uniform—
Were you saying something? Not Captain Farnsworth?
Scotty? How stupid of me! He's on the Navy team, of course.
They're going to begin. I'm so excited! I wonder if that is
Constance Fethrill, with the red hat? Who do you suppose
will win? I do adore red hats—though hers doesn't become
her one bit. Oh, yes, indeed, it was a perfectly splendid tackle.
I'm so glad I came! There's Agnes Berry in the next section.
Don't you think she's pretty? Why don't they start playing
again? I'm so excited I can't wait. Some one hurt? Why,
they're carrying him off. Poor fellow! What a perfectly
filthy pair of gloves I have. But I am so dead broke I really
can't afford another pair. I have such a time getting fitted.
What? Oh, no, my hands are very large. Don't you think
they are large? Oh, you nice boy! My hands are a perfect
joke in our family. Goodness! what are they doing now?
A touch-down! How exciting! And now they're going to kick
a goal from the field. Do you ever go to the dances at Belheim?
Don't you just love them? Why, the half is over. How disappointing! But now we can talk. I've been so interested I
haven't said a word. What do you think of the Navy team?
I'm just so keen about them. Of course they're not nearly so
fine as Pennsylvania. Hadn't Pennsylvania a perfectly glorious
team? I was so afraid they wouldn't beat Haverford. Charlie
Tuppover goes to Haverford, and is always talking about how
fine it is. I just hate it. Really I do." (Exclamation points,

italics, question-marks, etc., continue until 5.20 P.M.) "Oh, it's been just heavenly! I can never, never, thank you for taking me. Be sure and come to see me soon. I do enjoy football games."

—ANONYMOUS, *The Punch-Bowl*, University of Pennsylvania.

A Pious Remonstrance

To the Editor of The Punch-Bowl:

SIR: It seems to me that the attention of the fire inspectors should be called to the University chapel. The condition of the exits is frightful. What would happen if a fire should break out in that death-trap, crowded to the very doors by men, compelled against their will to go? Think of the awful destruction, the men trampled to death, the men burned, roasted, and fried, while vainly beating against the locked doors, which Pomp, blissfully ignorant, does not open? Think of the hundreds of men, urged into the room by threats—the flower of our youth—who would perish in the passing of a moment! It is criminal beyond measure that such a thing should be— that the trustees, the faculty, the dean should allow men to be packed so tightly in such a sepulcher. It is a time to take action. The chapel is crammed full with twenty times the men who want to be there. If the trustees, the faculty, the dean were humane, if they were considerate, if they valued the lives of the men who pay tuition, they would cut down this number four-fifths. Probably this knowledge of the awful danger that lies lurking there is the real cause that keeps them from attending and swelling the list of possible victims. A proper petition might succeed in having them restrict the number as we have suggested. Even this would not be any too small an assembly.

It is hardly possible that more than fifty men, in case of fire, could escape from the chapel without loss of life. Therefore, the student body should rise up and say, "No more than fifty men should be allowed in chapel," and persist until their request is granted. There might be some consolation in being burned up in a theater, because you go of your own free will, but in the chapel— We might take up the cry of half a century ago, and say, "Fifty or fight," and get justice.

Respectfully yours,

BROTHERS OF VERITAS.

—*The Punch-Bowl*, University of Pennsylvania.

A Lost Opportunity

OH, gay Bacchus, you mad fellow!
  It was always queer to me
How you got o'er being mellow,
  When you went upon a spree.

How'd you keep your head from swelling,
  When Silenus and his crew
Brought you to your sylvan dwelling,
  Loaded with ambrosial brew?

Seltzer then was not invented,
  To reduce the size of heads;
When filled with Olympic cocktails
  You were gently put to bed.

Did you have a secret potion,
　　Brewed in some sequestered glade,
Treasured as a sacred lotion,
　　Guarded by some sylvan maid?

Had you lived in later ages,
　　And had brought your secret down,
You'd have quickly made your fortune,
　　In 'most any college town.

　　　　—RIANT, '93, *Wrinkle*, University of Michigan.

The Darktown Nine

WASHINGTON JOHNSON LELAND FINE
Were de capt'in ob de Darktown nine;
An' de Darktown nine, 'twixt yo' an' me,
Were de bestest nine yo' eber did see.

De principlest game dey had to play
Were with the Giants from Hamtown way.
An' dey wanted to win dat game so bad,
An' dey betted all de money dey had,
An' dey asked de girls to see dem play,
An' watch de Darktowns win de day.

Fifteen innings wid nevah ah sco';
Dey played der hardest, an' even mo'.
When de Hamtown capt'in made a hit,
An' de Hamtown 'habitants had a fit,
An' de Hamtown pitcher brought him in,
An' dat was where dere grief begin.

College Humor

Wid two men out in de second half,
'Mid de Darktown's 'habitants low-down chaff,
Wid one man on bases, an' he on first,
A low-down niggah by name of Thirst,
De Darktown capt'in came to bat,
An' dusted de base off wid his hat.

"Strike one!" yelled de umpire.   I thought I'd faint,
An' only murmured, "Oh, no, it ain't."
"Strike two!" I heard without surprise,
An' den I just done close my eyes,
When—bang!—it sounded like a gun,
Our capt'in knocked a clean home run.

Washington Johnson Leland Fine
Were de capt'in ob de Darktown nine.
An' de Darktown nine, 'twixt yo' an' me,
Were de bestest nine yo' eber did see.
    —E. B. MASON, in *The Princeton Tiger.*

L'Envoi

Go, pretty Rose, and to her tell
  All I would say, could I but see
The slender form I know so well,
  The roguish eyes that laughed at me.

And when your fragrance fills the room,
  Tell her of all I hope and fear;
With every breath of sweet perfume,
  Whisper my greetings in her ear.

But, Roses, stay—there is one thing
   You must not mention (don't forget,
For it might be embarrassing),
   And that is, you're not paid for yet!
                    —E. B. REED, in *The Yale Record*.

The Flight of Time

"TEMPUS fugit," said the Romans;
Yes, alas, 'tis fleeting on;
         Ever coming,
         Ever going,
Life is short, and soon 'tis gone.

But as I think of next vacation,
Poring o'er these lessons huge,
         Ever harder,
         Ever longer,
All I say is, "Let her fuge!"
                    —J. K. BLAKE, in *The Yale Record*.

I Doubt It

WHEN a pair of red lips are upturned to your own,
   With no one to gossip about it,
Do you pray for endurance to let them alone?
   Well, maybe you do—but I doubt it.

College Humor

When a sly little hand you're permitted to seize,
    With a velvety softness about it,
Do you think you can drop it with never a squeeze?
    Well, maybe you do—but I doubt it.

When a tapering waist is in reach of your arm,
    With a wonderful plumpness about it,
Do you argue the point 'twixt the good and the harm?
    Well, maybe you do—but I doubt it.

And if by these tricks you should capture a heart,
    With a womanly softness about it,
Will you guard it and keep it, and act the good part?
    Well, maybe you will—but I doubt it.
        —ANONYMOUS, in *The Yale Literary Magazine*.

Logic and the Co-Ed

SHE got on a car going down-town. She was a freshman, and when the conductor came around after her nickel she said:

"Does this car go to Camp Randall?"

"No, it goes down-town," was the reply.

"But it says on the front, 'Football at Camp Randall to-day'; and doesn't it go there?"

"Yes," said the conductor. "It says 'Boston Baked Beans' on one of the signs on the inside, but the car doesn't go to Boston."

The young girl got off at the next corner.
        —*The Sphinx*, University of Wisconsin.

A Football Song

I

THEY talk of joy in fighting
  'Mid whistling shot and shell;
They rhyme of bliss in love's sweet kiss,
  A bliss that none can tell;
For ages they've been lilting
  The praise of ruby wine—
All joys most rare, but none compare
  With tacklin' 'hind the line.

II

Give me the football battle,
  The captain's signal call,
The rush that fills the heart with thrills,
  The line that's like a wall.
Give me the hard-fought scrimmage,
  The joy almost divine,
When like a rock we stand the shock
  And tackle 'hind the line.

III

The muse has long been singing
  The joy the half-back feels
When like a flash he makes a dash
  And shows the "bunch" his heels.

284

College Humor

His joy may be ecstatic;
   It can't be more than mine,
When with a smile amid the pile
   I tackle 'hind the line.

IV

To smash the interference
   Fills me with heartfelt glee;
To make a lunge and stop a plunge
   Is more than gold to me.
In running with the pigskin,
   I ne'er was known to shine,
But I can hew my way clear through,
   And tackle 'hind the line.

V

There may be joys in heaven
   More tender and more tame,
But I don't care to go up there
   Unless they play the game.
There's gridirons down in Hades,
   But even there I'd pine
To be once more on this fair shore,
   To tackle 'hind the line.
            —*The Sphinx*, University of Wisconsin.

Drinking-Song

You may say that Lachrymæ Christi
   Is a potion most divine;
You may praise the wine of Asti,
   Or claret of '59;
You may talk of your golden sherry,
   Of Heidsieck, dry and clear,
But a good drink and a merry
   Is plain Milwaukee beer.

'Tis a strong yet mild potation,
   But let that merit pass—
Its noblest commendation
   Is, "Just five cents a glass!"
Away with your costly Rhenish!
   With Chablis, good but dear,
And, waiter, my glass replenish
   With plain Milwaukee beer.
       —Anonymous, in *The Williams' Argo.*

Aunt Phœbe's Remonstrance

My *missis!* You gwine to marry *her*, you say!
   'Fo' Gord, now, marster, you's foolin' me, I knows.
Gwine tek dat little chile o' our'n away!
Why, she ain't nuthin' mo'n a chile!
You go back home and wait a while,
    Untel she grows.

College Humor

Why, marster, 'twa'n't but little while ago
   Dat I fuss hel' her in ole missis' room;
An' now you tells me she's done grow'd up? Sho!
Dat chile ain't no mo' fittin' fer
To marry you, I tell you, sir,
      Dan dis here broom.

She sholy was a fine-raised chile, I knows,
   Kaze I help raise her, sir; I brung her up.
When she wa'n't mo'n ten years ole, I s'pose,
Ole miss' use' stan' her by de wall,
'N' she'd say de twelb commandments all
      Widout a stop.

An' when I use' to tek her up to bade,
   Jes' sharp at eight—old miss' wus punkshall, sho—
I'd tek her in my lap an' comb her hade,
An' den I'd tell de stories to her
'Bout raslin' Jacob an' Marse Noah
      An' his rainbow.

One day ole marster tuck her off to school,
   Whar de gret folks had dere chillen larn.
When she come back, she'd set on dat dar stool,
'N' play dat piany tell it soun'
Fit like Brer Gabriel done come down
      Here wid his harn.

An' now you's gwine to tek my chile away?
   What's me 'n' ole miss' gwine do widout her den?
What make dat you cyarnt come down here an' stay?

Gwine tek dat preshus lam' wid you,
Fum miss' and her ole mammy, too—
    Say, marster, when?

Not 'fo' nex' fall! Oh, t'ank de Lord ob Grace!
  Kaze we's gwine hab her fer a little while!
When she's done gone, 'twon't be de same ole place;
But we befo' de Lord mus' bow.
Thankee, marster—lemme go now
    An' fin' my chile.

—R. F. WILLIAMS, JR., in *The Virginia University Magazine.*

Two of a Kind

SOFTLY the evening breezes
  Blew through the leaves overhead,
And the fireflies flashed like diamonds,
  The robins had gone to bed.

And there, in the gathering twilight,
  Swinging listlessly to and fro,
With one little foot just moving
  To make the hammock go,

She seemed to my loving spirit
  Like some mystical maiden of old,
With the eyes shining soft in the starlight,
  And her tresses like beaten gold.

288

And I sat at her feet adoring,
  Not daring a word to say,
Lest the beautiful charm should be broken,
  And the vision should vanish away.

But I longed to be sitting beside her,
  And pour in her listening ear
The words which burned in my bosom,
  And her whispered answer to hear.

"Fair maid, I beseech thee, tell me,
  Is there room enough for two
To sit and swing in the hammock,
  Should I come and swing with you?"

In her eyes burned a softer radiance,
  And gently her head inclined,
As she murmured, "Oh, yes, thrice plenty,
  But only for two of a kind."
      —H. W. BANKS, in *The Williams' Argo.*

A Merry, Blue-Eyed Laddie

A MERRY, blue-eyed laddie goes laughing through the town,
  Singing, "Hey, but the world is a gay, gay place!"
And every little lassie smooths her tumbled locks a-down,
And brings out all her dimples and hides away her frown,
  And lays aside her broom and mop, the bonnie boy to chase,
  Singing, "Hey, but the world is a gay, gay place!"

But away the blue-eyed laddie goes to seek another town,
　Singing, "Hey, but the world is a gay, gay place!"
Then every dimple vanishes, and back comes every frown,
And every little lassie folds away her Sunday gown,
　With tear-drops trickling sadly down her woful little face,
　Sighing, "Hey, but the world is a sad, sad place!"
　　—JULIET WILBUR TOMPKINS, in *The Vassar Miscellany.*

An Echo of Junior Week

IT was during the dessert course. He had been sitting next to her for the last hour and a half, and was deeply conscious of the beautiful contour of her arms and shoulders.

"Do you know," she said suddenly, "I've been in misery for a week. Sometimes I could almost scream with the pain."

"Why, what is the matter?" he exclaimed sympathetically.

"I was vaccinated a while ago, and it has taken dreadfully."

His eyes fell and his gaze was curious. But he saw no scar.

"Why, where were you vaccinated?" he asked impetuously.

She raised her eyebrows and smiled sweetly.

"In New York," she replied.

　　—ANONYMOUS, in *The Cornell College Widow.*